Sugared and Spiced 2
100 Monologues for Girls

by Mary Depner
Edited by Sally L. Depner

Jelliroll, Inc.
www.Jelliroll.com

A Jelliroll Book
Published by Jelliroll, Inc.
Fort Lauderdale, Florida
www.jelliroll.com

ISBN-978-0-9883488-2-0

**Sugared and Spiced 2
100 Monologues for Girls**

by Mary Depner
Edited by Sally L. Depner

Jelliroll, Inc.
www.Jelliroll.com

Dedication

This book is dedicated to the memory of my grandmother and her sisters, the Rowland girls: Myrtle, Violet, and Ethel.

Foreward

I wrote this sequel to *Sugared and Spiced, 100 Monologues for Girls* because of the popularity of the first book. I'm happy to say that it seems girls have found the monologues entertaining and useful. I've also been contacted by parents and teachers requesting to use the monologues for audition or performance purposes. As I mentioned in the first *Sugared and Spiced*, I think it's important for the actress performing these monologues to develop a backstory for her character. The monologues allow you that freedom and a backstory that you create will give your performance an extra level of depth and uniqueness. I also hope that some of the monologues are thought-provoking and may encourage conversations regarding feelings, experiences....What it's like to be a girl in the world today.

Sugared and Spiced 2, 100 Monologues for Girls

Table of Contents

Girl Party 10
Mahalo 11
Room for Improvement 13
Skate Board Fantasy? 15
A Little R-E-S-P-E-C-T Please! 17
Millie the Matchmaker 19
This Isn't Easy 21
Enough Already 22
Whatsa Matter with Me? 23
Chicken Soup is Thicker Than a Carrot Stick 24
A Girl and Her Dog 26
The Problem with Me 29
Tutu Tantrum 30
Never a Dull Moment – 32
Maybe Baby 34
Let's Pretend 35
Like, Totally! 37
The End 39
What She Did This Summer 40
Bucolic Blues 41
Someday 42
Annie's Acting and Babysitting Service Extraordinaire 44
Life's Like That 46
Funeral for a Friend 48
The Wedding Dress 50
The Domino Effect 52
The Secret 54

The Chocolate Milk Test	56
One Sheep, Two Sheep, Red Sheep, Blue Sheep	57
Life with Father	59
The Loneliest Girl in the World	61
The Noodle with the Poodle	62
The Snaggle-Toothed Dragon	63
Summer Sisters	65
To Be Me	66
The Doll House	67
Herbie Illman's Magic Spell	69
My Life, The Musical	70
A Month Away from Home	71
Dear Uncle Jimmy	73
My Favorite Memory	75
I'm Just a Girl	77
On the Phone with Tara	78
The Curious Case of the Snotty-Rottens	79
Honest Feedback	82
Lost in Space	84
Love is an Action Verb	85
Sometimes It's Crazy Being Me	87
My Dream	89
The Last Laugh	90
Built-in Babysitter	91
Wonder Girl	92
Things Change	93
My Dad the Cat – Well Sort Of	95
She Said, Yawning	96
Myrtle the Diva Turtle	97
When I Grow Up	99
Robot-Proof Me	100
Scruffy Come Home	101
Rhoda the Rhymer	103

The Monster in Me   104
Movies and Meaning   106
I'd Rather Be Tina Fey   107
The "Why" Baby   109
Are You Afraid to Listen?   110
Sisters   111
Tea for Two   113
Bonkers   114
Twelve Going on Thirty   115
Who Is the Real Me?   116
Once Upon a Time   117
Shy   118
Love Happens   120
Things I Can't Say   121
Hello Tree   122
Anyone but Me   123
Literal Lottie   124
There's a Monster in My Macaroni   125
The Not-Nicest Camper of Them All   127
There's a Sailboat in my Soup   129
Dear Mable Massiwash-Macabee   131
You'll Never Guess   133
My Short Story Came to Life   135
Tchaikovsky and Me   137
The Beginning, Middle, and the End   138
Something is Wrong With Me   139
The Worst Part   140
The Perfect Boy   142
Mother Knows Best?   143
WYSIWYG   144
Stuck with That   146
Your Armpits May Be Crazy, but My Big Toe is Psycho   147
My Happy Ending   148

33 Things   150
All I Want for Christmas   151
Hooked on Writing   152
A Valentine from March   154
I'm Not Impressed   155
Just Friends   156
The Last Day of School   157

About The Author   158

Girl Party

My specialty is mashed potatoes and sauerkraut. Huh? I said my specialty is mashed potatoes and sauerkraut. What do you mean, what's that supposed to mean? It means I make mashed potatoes and sauerkraut really, really well. What's so funny? What is so…You're goofy. Yeah, you. You asked me what I was bringing to the party and I'm bringing mashed potatoes and sauerkraut. They're my special…Okay, you're all jerks. You're all…so what? So what if it's a girl party. That doesn't mean we all have to bake pink cupcakes or something. I'm a girl and I eat mashed potatoes and sauerkraut. And I can make them myself, too. I don't have to wait for my mother to get home to eat, like some people, not to mention any names, Tara! Yeah, I know that's real food. So, what? Just cause it's a Girl Party doesn't mean we can't have real food. We can't just eat cupcakes and cream puffs and pizza. I may be weird, but I get tired of pizza. Okay, I said I'm weird. Yeah, I know that's what we did last year and I still remember it. Cause I was starving the whole time! I don't care what you guys, oops I mean Girls, think! I'm bringing real food for real girls to our real Girl Party. If it makes you happy, I can make the mashed potatoes pink. (thinks for a minute) A little beet juice will do the trick. Yeah, beets! Yeah, I'll make the mashed potatoes pink and I'll bring some beet salad too. What do you mean, ewww. Listen, legend may say that little girls are made of Sugar and Spice and everything nice, but this girl is made up of broccoli, cauliflower, beets, potatoes, sauerkraut and stew and…on top of it all, a pink cupcake or two.

Mahalo

Sometimes you wonder if you're dreaming. If this stuff is real in front of your eyes that's happening to you. I feel that way a lot! I mean, can all of this junk be happening to me, or is this just a bad dream. Like, when I found out that we were moving just before I started fifth grade. It took me two long years to make friends at Edenshire Elementary, and then bam, here we go again. Moving. And, no matter what my dad say's, it's never any fun. Not to me. Or, the time I got the flu - just in time for the end of year school trip. And then it happened again the next year. And the next. You say to yourself at times like that, this can't be real. Things can't really, truly be this bad. Am I a magnet for trouble? I say things like that to myself all the time. No, no, this can't be real. I'm going to wake up and I'll be on the bus with all the kids going to the park. Or, I'm really on the airplane flying to DC, not in this bed with a fever. But, unfortunately, it's not the case. Reality hits you in the face like a flying saucer…or, maybe a frying pan. Ouch! It really actually hurts. But, last month, something different happened. I don't know what we did to deserve it, but mom and dad took us all on an amazing trip to Hawaii. And, I didn't get sick. I got to go! And we all had an amazing time. We went to the beach, and the water was so warm and so beautiful. And when we weren't at the beach we were at the pool. We even made friends there with a Hawaiian family staying at the hotel who had moved to Florida and came back to see some old friends. Their son was really cute and he taught me some Hawaiian words. I mean, everyone knows Aloha, but he taught me what it really means

Continued

and he taught me to say Mahalo too. That means thank you.
He also taught me how to surf. A little. And just a few times
during the vacation I had to stop and ask myself, is this real, or
is this just a dream? But, it was real. And finally, this time I was
soooo glad. I love Hawaii, and…all the people there. But I love
my parents most of all. I hope they know how much it meant to
me. Mahalo Mom and Dad.

Room for Improvement

What does it look like I'm doing? I'm painting, nitwit. I'm
sorry! I was only kidding. You're not a nitwit. I'm just getting a
bit grouchy cause my arm is tired. Wanna help? Yeah, there's
another brush over there. This is gonna be my new room. Yeah,
cool, right? I'm so glad that Sam went to college. I mean, I love
her and all that. She's an awesome big sister, but big sisters can
be overrated sometimes. Especially when they're in high school
and they're the Homecoming Queen and the Prom Queen and
basically the biggest star in the universe. I mean my parents
always told us to "let our little light shine," but Sam's light is
colossal. Yeah, COLOSSOL. My light, on the other hand, is
about the size of a firefly. Or, maybe even smaller. I'm like the
glint in a flea's eye when it gets a bright idea. Or, like the glow
in a microscopic organism's heart when it falls in love, (sighs)
Of course things will be different when I'm in high school. I
might be like Sam, but it's actually looking like I might not.
Right now, I don't think I'm on the same trajectory. That's what
Mr. Ross told my mom at her teacher/parent conference the
other day. Yeah, he actually compared me to Sam and then he
said I have "room for improvement." Of course mom told me.
We tell each other everything. Mom said he meant it well, but I
know that's just Mr. Ross's way of saying that I totally stink. At
Math, that is. Not personally. I shower at least once a week. Just
kidding, nitwit! I'm sorry, I shouldn't have said that again. It's a
rotten habit. Calling you names. I'm not perfect. I totally admit
that. But, then again, neither are you, right! That's why we're
friends, right? I couldn't stand you if you didn't have any flaws.

Continued

You know you have flaws, right? Like…(thinks for a minute then laughs) you're a lousy painter for one. Look! You've got more paint on your clothes than on the wall. (Laughing) I think your mother's going to kill you! (looks down at her clothes) Ooops. I think my mother is going to kill me! Oh well, (starts painting again) Maybe we can tell our mothers that we did it in art class and get old Ms. Feinstein in trouble. I'm just joking stupid. I wouldn't do that. Neither would you. I mean we're flawed but we're not jerks. We don't have that much room for improvement.

Skate Board Fantasy?

I used to be that girl. (points out the window) See, the one on the skateboard. Yeah, I used to be like her. Really good. So good that the boys wouldn't challenge me anymore. Cause they didn't want to lose to a girl. That's my board, over there in the corner. I might not ever take it out again. The doctor said it might be too dangerous. It's only been two months since the accident, but it feels like… a year, maybe two years ago. And it feels like yesterday. I think I just sounded like my grandmother, didn't I? That's definitely something she would say. Maybe I'm getting old sitting in this chair all day watching the other kids have fun. How long have you been cleaning houses? Your whole life? Even when you were a little girl? How come? That's okay. I know you're busy. You have a whole house to clean. I just… like talking to you. It gets lonely in here sometimes. At first some of the kids and teachers came by with cards, and the principal called the house once too. I didn't really want to see anybody then. I was in so much pain. And my mother got so angry because the accident happened at school. I heard her arguing with the principal when he called, and when she came back in my room it looked like she was crying. (pauses, watching the kids outside) I wish they'd all come over now. Now, I wouldn't mind so much. But they've probably already forgotten all about me. Especially now, that I'm being home-schooled and I'm never going back. Yes, thank you, you can take my tray. That was delicious. Did you make it? Ah! Delicious! Yes, thank you! Okay, I'll ring the bell if I need anything. Thanks. (looks out the window, then to self)

Continued

I'm going to get back out there. I know I am. I don't care what the doctor says. It's going to happen. I'm going to get well, and strong and be better than ever. I'll show them. And me.

A Little R-E-S-P-E-C-T Please!

(running out of the auditions to meet Carol) Carol! (squealing with excitement) I'm getting really close to getting this part. This is my third call back. Well, there's a lot of competition and a ton of people trying out. Everyone loves Mr. Petrie. He's so cool. And, the play is so awesome. There are sooo many good parts. At first, I thought I wanted to be Betty, but then I realized that would be too easy for me, so I'm going out for Doctor Pizza. It's a funny part and it's a stretch role because I've never played a grown up before. It could be a boy's part or a girl's part. Obviously. There is nothing in the script that says Doctor Pizza is a man. Not one single word. (She does a HUGE eyeball roll.) I'm SURE. I read the play like (waving three fingers in front of Carol's face) three times. Sidney Greene is really good though. I'm afraid he's going to get it. (frowns and shakes her head) Everyone thinks he's soooo funny. And even when he isn't funny the girls all giggle (imitates a silly giggle), so Mr. Petrie thinks Sidney's the funniest kid in town. But all the girls just think he's cute. I have no idea why. I don't think he's good looking at all. (sticks her tongue out after that and says) Yuck! I never did! What? That's not true! I NEVER HAD A CRUSH ON SIDNEY GREENE. You TAKE THAT BACK! I am NOT being sensitive. I'm just telling the truth. If you say that one more time, (long pause)… I'm never speaking to you again. I can too! I am perfectly capable of not talking in general and not talking specifically to you. No, I do not like to talk too much. Nope, just because we live in the same house – doesn't matter. Just because you're my older sister – doesn't matter. If

Continued

you say that one more time, I am never….That's it! (puts her hand up) I am zipping my lip. (makes the zipper movement across her lips, then calls over to Francine) Francine! Is your mother picking you up? Can I get a ride with you? My sister? (looks over her shoulder for a second and quickly turns back to Francine) That USED to be my sister, but currently she is not. Yes, I know. I hear her. I know she is talking to me, but at this time I am not. Talking. To her. Nor will I EVER speak to her again.

She is immature. And un-sensitive. And COMPLETELY WRONG. (getting emotional) I wish…I wish…I wish I could get some RESPECT around here. I'm an actress. I have feelings, and I don't like it when people assume that my sensitive nature is a flaw. That just because I think someone's a good actor that means I like him or have a crush on him. Or whatever. I am a serious actress going out for the most difficult role I've ever played and I'm doing really well against some really tough competition. I mean, sometimes a girl, whether she gets to be Doctor Pizza or not, deserves a little respect. It's stressful auditioning and the last thing I need is to add to this stress with false accusations of crushes and nonsense and… Carol, I hate you!

Millie the Matchmaker

Okay, that'll be fifty cents and then we can get started. So, you like Steven Strombolli and he doesn't even know you're alive. Is that the problem? Oh, okay, well, something like that. Okay, first, let's see what category he fits in (thumbing through cards), boy next door? No. Boy on the next floor? No. Oh, what's that? Boy on floor 8 and you're on floor 2? Oh, well this is an easy one then. You have to catch him on his way home from school. You get on the elevator and accidentally miss your floor and make small talk with him. Yes, I'm afraid you have to talk to him. (looking through notes quickly) Let's see I have it right here…somewhere…yes it was in the December issue of Pre-teen Scene last year. It says the key to starting a friendship, or building a friendship of any kind, is to talk to the person you want to be friends with. Yes, friends. Oh, I know you have a crush on him and you want to be Valentines and all that lovey-dovey stuff. But seriously? You think you can do that without being friends first? Really? Look, they don't call me Millie the Matchmaker for nothing kiddo. I mean, sure, I may be a kid, but I've done my research and that's how I can take fifty cents from sweet kids like you and still go to sleep at night with a clear conscience. Listen kid, this crush stuff is for the birds. You can't like the guy unless you know the guy, and you can't know him unless you TALK to him. And, maybe he won't be easy to talk to cause he's just a kid. You know some of us are. Just normal kids who do normal stupid kid things. And then there's kids like me. Well, I don't want to say ab-normal kids, cause that has negative connotations. Oh, you can look it up later. But, really

Continued

we're not abnormal, we're just special. Some of us have lemonade stands, some mow lawns, some code software and then others, make matches. (looks at her watch) Oops. Looks like your time's up. Unless you have another fifty cents, maybe?

This Isn't Easy

This isn't easy, Andrew. Coach is right when he says nothing worth having ever is. But wow, when you win those competitions, you know it is worth it. I know. I know. I'm sure you get sick of getting advice from everyone and taking it from me is probably the worst. I mean what guy wants advice from his little sister? But this is different. This is something I've been through. Remember? I've been competing since I was five. Yes, I know that you're aware of that. But I've experienced the competition and at this level it can be very, very, very tough. You'll skate your best and you'll know you're at your best and then somebody else will skate better. It can happen, and it does happen. You have to be mentally tough. You have to remember that you learn from everything. You learn from losing. You learn to keep working. You learn that the next time you skate, it could be you that surprises everyone and takes the lead. You have what it takes, Andrew. You have all the strength and the talent, and I know you have the determination. But you are sooo used to winning in everything else. In soccer, in football, in Math! Everything always comes easy for you. But, take it from your favorite little sister. If you don't take skating seriously, you'll be skating on thin ice. Brother, this one isn't easy.

Enough Already

I've had enough already. Enough with homework. Enough with school. Enough with learning the golden rule. Uggh. It's a beautiful day out there. I would soooo rather be at the beach. At this rate I'll never be done. I should never have stayed out sick so long with the flu. Bonnie Maeder's mother makes her go to school every single day, even if she has a fever. I bet she never had a mound of make-up work like this - as big as Mount Everest.

Look at this, I'm behind two chapters in reading. I've got to write 15 pages in my journal to make up for lost time. How can I do that? How can I possibly write about my life for 15 pages, when my life is suddenly nothing but sitting in this dark room, looking out at that dreamy sky wishing I were anybody but me? (sighs) It must be so nice to not care about grades. Not care about schoolwork, not care about anything but your tan. Why can't I be that girl? Well, I mean, not completely that girl. Then, I guess, I'd fail all my classes and then, I'd have to go to summer school and then, uggh. That's not for me. Hmm. Let's see, Dear Journal, Today I've decided enough is enough! I'm going to hunker down and focus and get through all of my work, so I can be free. Free to be me. No more complaining. No more whining. Enough already!

Whatsa Matter with Me?

Everyone else gets "stay as sweet as you are." Not me. Not
once. Look at my yearbook. Go ahead look. Do you see one?
Can you find one? I'll give you ten buckaroos if you can find
one "Stay as sweet as you are." Go ahead. Try! You can't find
one can you. Can you? What'ya mean I'm not sweet! I'm not
just sweet I'm SUPER sweet. Take that back! Say I'm sweet or
I'll give you a black eye! Thank you! That's better. Boy, I just
don't understand it. These kids at this school sure are dumb.
They think Melissa Fritterhead is so great. Yeah, yeah, Fritteray.
Whatever! I don't know, I can't say that name. I think Fritterhead sounds better anyway. But, gee whiz, she gets picked for
everything! And if she doesn't get picked she volunteers. Even
for the stuff nobody else wants. (imitates Melissa with a sticky
syrupy voice) "Miss Castaneda, I'll take out the garbage if you
need me to." Naw, I'm just making that up. Nobody takes out
the garbage, but Mr. Needlehead. Okay, Mr. Needlemeyer. Say,
when did you become such a nice guy. Where's your sense of
humor? You used to get my jokes. You don't laugh at nothing I
say no more. Oh, okay, anything I say no more. Gee whiz, what
is it? Don't you like me no more? Whatsa matter with me?

Chicken Soup is Thicker Than a Carrot Stick

My report is on the improper usage of popular sayings that people misunderstand and use the wrong way.
For example: A Jack of All Trades, If You Feed a Cold, and Blood is Thicker than Water. A lot of people for example think that Blood is Thicker means that your family ties are stronger than the ties you make with people you choose –like your friends - that you aren't born with. But that's not what it means. I'm not really sure what it means cause I didn't get that far in my research. But I encourage you to look it up. I'm pretty sure that you're using it wrong once in a while, I know my mother does it all the time. The next one is A Jack of All Trades is a Master of None, or something like that. I could tell you exactly if Mrs. Nickels let us use note cards, but since this report is supposed to be all from memory, that's the best I can do. I encourage you to look it up because just about everyone gets this one wrong. I just can't remember why. The next saying that gets all messed up is Feed a Cold and Starve a Fever. This one I remember. People think this one means that you should starve a cold and feed a fever. Just like it sounds. So, that's why your mother keeps you home from school and gives you all sorts of chicken soup and Hamburger Helper when your burning up, but if you've only got the sniffles she gives you a carrot stick for lunch and makes you go to school. So, I'm happy to say that this one does not mean what it sounds like. I told my mother as soon as I found out! It means, if you starve a cold you'll get a fever. It really does! So, you can get chicken soup and Hamburger Helper without your forehead practically being on fire.

Continued

It's true. I encourage you to look it up.

A Girl and Her Dog

I'm reading *Moby Dick* right now. It's probably the third time
I've read it and I'm actually getting more out of it than I did
before. Before, I remember rushing and wanting to get to the
part where Ishmael gets on the whaling ship and goes out to
sea. I wanted to read about Ahab and Starbuck and the great
whale. But this time, I'm reading it at a slower pace and it's
been amazing to me. First, I thought it was strange that I decided to pick the book up again in November and when I started
reading, there it was on the first page of the book – Ishmael
talking about November. And, then he refers to the election
of the President of the United States. And when did Melville
write this book? Somewhere around 1850, I think? How is it
that this novel could suddenly feel so connected to me and to
the world around me? This time when I read the words, I felt
as if I'd seen a ghost, but not a frightening ghost, more like a
friendly ghost, or maybe a relative ghost, or maybe another
version of me. I hope I'm not boring you. It's so good of you
to listen. I feel that I can tell you, that I will always tell you in a
way that I can't with others, the truth about myself. You know
with others I can't be open. I don't like to be…vulnerable. To
be judged. But, I'm talking so much today. Maybe it is that
glass of grape juice I had in one of mother's best wine glasses
today with lunch. Snow days are lonely in the house and I feed
myself and find myself pouring a nice glass of grape juice and
using the crystal just like mother. She wouldn't stand for it if
she were here…me using her best crystal. But, it's a snow day
for children and a work day for her. "Delivering babies can-

not be put on hold for the snow," mother would say. Ah, but
I digress. I was about to tell you about something I read about
reincarnation and the past life that I'm certain was mine. I had
a dream that made me think that I might have lived before, and
it made me happy to believe that I had lived before and might
live again, but it surprised me and disappointed me too. What
if I was once a cabin boy on a whaling ship or something like
that? Yes, I think I might have been a cabin boy once with a
very harsh life of work and drudgery. Not what I am today – a
spoiled, bored child of a well-bred, well-intentioned mother
and an absent father who sends lovely appropriate gifts on all
of the most-appropriate occasions. And…I am in… a constant
state of disappointment. Each and every gift that I receive
makes me feel…resentful…and angry. I'm not…really sure
why. My Sunday School teacher, always says that we should
all have an "attitude of gratitude." And I want to be grateful. I really truly do. But, something inside me won't allow it.
It's almost like what mother says is true…it's not in my DNA.
(sighs) That glass of grape juice is making me sleepy. I shouldn't
talk so much. You must be bored. I've been talking a great deal
of nonsense and you haven't said a word. Poor kitty, not only
have I spoiled life for you by giving you the most despicable
and humiliating name that any dog could wish for, I constantly
bore you at every turn. It's so good of you to lie still and listen.
If mother ever gives me a real dog, I'm sure I won't have the
undivided attention that I so enjoy with you. So, you see, sometimes it is as mother says, we are better off not receiving the

Continued

things we ask for. It's like that old-time rock band once said, - oh what was it Kitty? I may not get the things that I want, but I probably have everything that I need. Something like that. Oh, poor Kitty, you're falling asleep. Let's say our prayers and have sweet dreams. (Lights out.)

The Problem with Me

(Yelling loudly over the wooden fence) Shake it, don't break it! (Ducks down laughing) Oh my gosh! Did they see me? Do you think they…(turns and peeks through the cracks in the fence) Jessica Martin is looking all over the place, so I know they heard me! This is so cool that you live right next to school. Oh, don't worry, you won't get in trouble. They have no idea where that came from. They can't see through the fence unless they have x-ray eyes. (Gets up and starts to dance around like a cheerleader – but kind of goofy) They can't see me doing this! Besides, it's the first day of cheerleading practice, and all they're thinking about is how LUCKY they were to get picked, and how CUTE they look in their matching shorts, and what JERKS all the rest of us were for even trying out. For even thinking we could be Cougarettes. Yeah, I tried out. Of course, I did. I do every year. And…of course, I never make it. Why? Cause I stink. No, I do. The problem with me is that I'm not coordinated. Well, I mean, I'm coordinated but I have trouble coordinating with everyone else. I mean, synchronizing. So, if I could be the ONLY cheerleader, I'd be great. But, the problem is there are a bunch of cheerleaders and you have to jump when they jump and move to the right and move to the left when they do. I just can't ever do it. So, I usually make the first cut when you do the cheer alone, but then when they put me in the group tryout? I'm outta there. Still, I'll probably try next year, too. It's like my mom always says, the problem with me is, I never learn.

Tutu Tantrum

This is it?! This is my costume?! Why?!! Why me?!! Mother!!
Come here! Mother!!! Come HERE! Mother, come here
NOW!!! Miss Nancy hates me! Look at this! Look at me! I look
like…like…a purple pickle! (to her little sister who is practically rolling on the floor laughing) Stop laughing, Allie! Wait till
you're old enough to be in a dance recital. When you get a…
a…purple pickle costume, and the rest of your whole entire
class gets to be beautiful, wonderful Can-Can dancers, wearing
cute little pink and red skirts with lacy under things, you won't
find it so funny! You won't laugh then! Get out of my room,
Allie! Get out! Mother make her leave!! I hate Miss Nancy! I
hate her. I'm not wearing this! I'm not! Why did Miss Nancy
give me this solo number? Right in the middle of the ensemble
routine. She made me think I was special. She told me she
wanted me to stand out! Well, I'll stand out alright. I'll be the
laughing stock of the whole recital. I can just hear the jokes
now! (in a funny voice) "Hey can I get a big purple sandwich
to go with this big purple pickle!" (to her mother who is trying
to calm her down) They will too make fun of me! I do look like
a pickle! I do!! No, I don't have it on wrong, Mother. I've been
dancing in recitals since I was three years old, so I'm pretty sure
I know how to put a costume on right by now! Backwards? No,
it's not. It is not…backwards (looks in mirror). It's…well…may-
be. Maybe. (Turns it around. Smiles weakly.) Oh! Well, that's a
little better. That's a little less like a pickle. Now I just look like a
purple olive. (with her funny voice again) "Excuse me waitress,
can you bring me the rest of my giant purple salad! Somehow

this giant purple olive rolled onto my table." (to her mother again) What? There's a hat in the box, too? Give me that! (Puts the hat on). Well, hey…that's kind of cute. It sort of brings out the color of my eyes, don't you think? Huh? There's a tutu too? Give me that! I didn't see that! I didn't see…(steps into it) ah-hhh! (looking in the mirror). I look….BEAUTIFUL!! (grinning from ear to ear and jumping up and down) I look absolutely… beautiful!! Everyone's going to be so jealous of me! I love Miss Nancy! She is the best!

Never a Dull Moment

Ah Silence. Solitude. These are what I value most. And these are not only a rare commodity in the Drexler-Buxner house, but they are indeed virtually extinct. Ever since my mother married Bill Buxner and his THREE sons and TWO daughters moved in – my step brothers and sisters. Yes, dear mother and Bill left on their honeymoon to Cancun, and while they were away Aunt Margaret and Uncle Fred orchestrated "the move." By the time Mother and Bill got back, we were all in our places with not-so-bright shining faces. To put it bluntly, this house is a zoo. No, it's a circus. It's…the worst. Oh, how I miss days gone by. You must forgive me while I wax nostalgic. In the days before the Buxner brood, that is B.B.B., I could sit for hours and write in my dear, dear, dear diary. Poor diary, how it must miss me now. In the quintessential quiet and supreme solitude of the morning I used to sit and write… simple thoughts. Just simple little things, such as… what I planned to do for the day. Something interesting that I read about in the news. Or something funny that Fluffy did. Then, in the serenity and stillness of the evening I would take time to leisurely recall the best, and sometimes the worst, moments of the day, contemplating the meaning. The meaning of it all. Perhaps pausing for a moment to dream about the future. Que sera, sera, sera. But now? The future my dear is here. And, now, in the past months, since that loud and boisterous wedding day, that July 4th wedding day, amid fireworks and obnoxiously loud wedding guests – my peaceful and tranquil life is no more. So, alas, I'm sitting here in the quietest place, the most silent spot I know, the corner of my closet, well, that is, the closet I now share with Brenda Buxner, with the door closed, in the dark. And, I won't even try to write. No, no, no, I have given up that luxury. But I will be thankful that I have a moment to...think. Yes, just to think an uninterrupted thought. Until Brenda looks for... a missing shoe... her favorite shirt, or...heaven only knows. This heavenly sanctuary is.... my last golden luxury.

Maybe Baby

Whenever I don't get what I want, my grandmother always tells me that it is probably for the best. You know, like, "Maybe, baby, it's a good thing you didn't make the cheerleading squad. If you had made it, you would have probably broken an arm or a leg, so see how lucky you are!" Or, "It's a good thing your dad didn't buy that puppy for you. He might have bitten the neighbors, or maybe got run over by a car!" And, she's right. Sometimes things do happen for a reason, I think. And, maybe we don't always know what's good for us. Maybe the thing we always wanted wouldn't have turned out the way we thought it would anyway. That's what I try to remember when things don't seem to go my way. Maybe they're going exactly the best way for me, but I just can't see it. Like last year when we moved here for my mother's job. I really, really didn't want to leave Stephen Foster Elementary and all my friends. But, maybe, if we'd stayed, something terrible would have happened. Maybe I would have found out that Rainy Rosenblatt was talking about me behind my back and wasn't really my BFF after all. That would have just killed me. You know? So, it's something to always keep in mind. Just because you didn't get your way, maybe you ought to be thankful after all. Sometimes, things work out for the best in the long run. It's just the short run that's hard when you wanted something so badly it makes your heart break in half, and you cry till you can't cry anymore. Sometimes it's hard to know just how lucky you are.

Let's Pretend

Hey, Rebecca, I know what we can do! Let's pretend this is a beauty salon. I'm the hair dresser and you can be the client. Oh, come on! We are not too old to pretend. My father says you are never too old to use your imagination, and that's what separates people from animals and all that. You know, our imaginations. Oh, come on, it will be fun! Okay, you can sit here, and I'll be… No wait, first I'll be the receptionist and you can check in at the desk. (in her best receptionist's voice) "Hello. It's a great day at Flo's salon, do you have an appointment?" (sighs, then in her own voice) Rebecca, I know you don't really have an appointment, but I still have to ask cause I'm not me, I'm the receptionist. Get it? It's pretend. I'm the receptionist and you're the client. Okay? So, you get to pretend that you have an appointment or you don't have an appointment. Okay. Let's try again. (Receptionist's voice) "Hello, it's a great day at Flo's salon, do you have an appointment? Oh, great. Can I get your Name?" (Sighs and then in her own voice) What do you mean your name is Rebecca? Yeah, I know your real name is Rebecca, but this isn't real. This is PRETEND. You have to make up a fake name like Gloria, or Linda. Yeah, that's it, like Mary Faye! That's a great name. Okay. (sighs) One more time. (receptionist's voice with a little less enthusiasm) "Hello, it's a great day at Flo's salon, do you have an appointment? Great. Can I get your name?" (in her own voice) Ugggh! What do you mean I know your name is Mary Faye! Of course I know your name is Mary Faye, but the receptionist doesn't know your name is Mary Faye! Uggh! Didn't anybody ever teach you how

Continued

to pretend? Okay, this is it! One more time, and if this doesn't work, I'm going home. (receptionist voice, but very irritated) "Hello, It's a rotten day at Flo's salon. Do you have an appointment? Great. Can I get your name? Oh, Mary Faye. Hmmm. Let's see. (looking at pretend schedule) Funny, but I don't see a Mary Faye here. I see a Gloria, and a Harriet, and a Lisa, but no Mary Faye. Are you sure you have the right day?" (In her own voice) Isn't this fun!

Like, Totally!

Macy isn't coming over cause she's mad at me. (shouting) I said, "Macy's not coming over. She's mad! (rolling her eyes now) No, not mad like a cow granny. Mad at me. MAD AT ME! Are you wearing your hearing aid? Where is it? Oh, jumping jelly beans did you lose your hearing aid again?! Okay. Okay. I'll help you find it. I said, I'LL FIND IT! (looks around for a minute and smiles and then starts to laugh) It's…it's… Granny….(picking up the hearing aid from a dish of berries and handing it to Granny) Granny, you dropped it in the bowl of berries again! I hope you didn't wash it when you rinsed the berries! (shaking her head) Granny, I think that bowl of berries is all yours. I hope you're hungry. I said, HAVE A BERRY!! AND PUT YOUR HEARING AID ON! I NEED TO TELL YOU ABOUT MACY! (pauses) So, Macy's mad at me and won't come over today. She says she won't ever come over again. Well, I don't know. I mean I do know why she's mad, but I don't think she should be. I didn't' do anything wrong! Well, I mean, not really. I was just playing the game. The game that Louise Teller had us play at her overnight birthday party. We put some names of kids at school in a bag, and some teachers too. Then we were supposed to draw out a name and try to imitate that person. Louise is the president of Junior Thespians and she's all into being an actress and everything, so I think she just wanted to show us how good she was at imitating everybody and then she'd win the prize. It was S'not Candy. Yes, your hearing aid is working. It is called S'not Candy. Isn't that gross. It's called that cause its sweets that are made out of

Continued

vegetables and not sugar, so it tastes like candy but it's not. Get it? S'not Candy. Anyway, you could either win that or some jar of face cream that her mother didn't want anymore, so I'm not sure why any of us agreed to play the game, but we all did. And I pulled Macy's name from the bag and now she isn't speaking to me. Well, I guess I'm pretty good at imitating Macy and she didn't like it at all. I kind stood like Macy does with her hands on her hips and I said (in Macy's voice) "Like, it's totally awesome that we like totally have no homework tonight cuz I'm like so sick of homework and like under no circumstances would I miss the last episode of like my favorite tv show, like once I figure out which one is my favorite, cuz, like I only watch 100 shows a week. Like, what else is there to do?" (in her own voice again) Well it went something like that. So, like, do you think she'll, like, ever forgive me? Like, totally?

The End

(In a deep grown up soap-opera voice) Drew, you're the reason that I never followed my dreams. After hours in therapy with Dr. Rolando I can see that now, and it's so clear, crystal clear. I couldn't possibly follow my dreams because I needed, or I thought I needed, security. And, stupidly, I thought that I found that in you. You, of all people, you the one pers... (sighs...exasperated, then in her real voice) Okay, what is it now?! Well, Jennifer, every time I get to that line you call cut. We aren't ever going to finish the scene are we? I beg your pardon? Really? Really? Okay. Let's see, first I didn't look dreamy enough when I said the word "dreams," then I wasn't saying Drew's name with the "appropriate amount of anger." Now you're telling me that I sound like a child when I'm supposed to be a thirty-year old woman. Well, I hate to break it to you Jennifer, but I have a news flash for you. I AM A CHILD! I. AM. A. CHILD. Why are we doing this play? I know I said this time you could be the director. I know I said that this time you could pick the script, but THIS? THIS is a a disaster! Excuse me? No! (trying not to totally lose her temper) No, Jennifer, I do not want to "hold on to my anger and try the scene again." I'm through. I quit! The End.

What She Did This Summer

Tomorrow we have to go back to school. My sister Jenna used to love that day. The first day back. Shopping for weeks before for new clothes. Wondering who would be in her class. This year, she's so different. She's like…someone I don't know. She's so quiet. Ever since she came back from camp. Stays in her room all day with strange music playing. Not the tunes we used to listen to together. It's like she…doesn't have any use for me anymore. My parents say she's just growing up, going through a phase. It's those "difficult teen years." I don't think so. I think… something happened. Something happened to her at camp. (sighs) Everyone thinks I'm being a baby and can't accept that she's leaving me behind. Maybe that's it. But the Jenna I know would never leave me behind. She would talk and laugh and tell me every little thing that happened to her and tell me how she felt. Even if she felt different. She wouldn't shut me out. She…just wouldn't. How can I make her know that whatever happened it's okay. She can tell me. She can tell…someone. She doesn't have to shut out the world and go away. I'm so afraid. I'm so afraid that…if we don't help her come out of this strange fog, that we'll never see her again. Jenna. You can talk to me. Please talk to me. Please tell me what you did this summer!

Bucolic Blues

I'm so lonely. I wish there was someone to call or something to do. Everyone's gone home to be with their families for the holiday except for me. It wasn't "possible" this year. Both of my parents are travelling for work and stuck in Europe. How terrible for them. But of course, mom says, "I'm so much better off here with the house mother and all my books." And "it's so terrific" that I can get ahead of everyone in my reading. So much better than spending hours on planes and in airports, just for a few measly moments at home. Where I would "surely die of absolute boredom." (sighs) It's such baloney. I hate this place. And, I think I've expressed that very clearly to everyone I know, especially my parents. But do they hear that? Apparently not. I know I helped pick this school, so it's partly my fault. It looked really good on the web, and our tour of the place seemed to go okay. I was just kind of hoping it would turn out to be every-thing they said it would be. "A boarding school that is truly a home away from home." "A lovely bucolic setting where friendships are made that last forever." Or, something like that. Bucolic. Hmph. I've had enough bucolic to last me a lifetime. I miss the city life. Honking horns in congested traffic. Graffiti on every corner. Trash on the ground. Smog in the air. Unfriendly people pushing past you on the sidewalk. (getting a bit teary) Oh gosh! I'm so homesick. I would gladly travel all day and all night just to be able to step out of a cab into a huge wad of gum. Honestly! This bucolic life is for the birds. Literally.

Someday

(Talking to her sister and imitating their mother) "Someday you'll understand just how much I sacrificed for you." If I
had a dollar for every time I heard mom say that I'd be a gazil-
lionaire. And you! With your "But, homework is easy for you!"
Since when? That's not true. I work hard at getting it done on
time and done right. What was that? Okay, I think I'm gonna
pretend that I didn't hear that! Uggh! I could…If you weren't
my little sister, I'd…You know, just because I spend a lot of time
at my desk doing homework doesn't mean I wouldn't like to
be doing other things. And just because I don't have friends
that come over after school doesn't mean I don't have friends.
My friends just happen to live far away and happen to be really busy, like me, doing homework, or taking music lessons,
or other constructive things. I don't hang out with the type of
kid you hang out with. You know. Yes, you do. Kids who don't
care. About anything but having fun. Like grades. Or, music.
Listening to music doesn't count. I mean, playing an instru-
ment. Or drawing. Your friends? Who draws? Oh, really? Amy
draws? Amy Kepner draws? Hmmm. I'd like to see some of
her art work someday. Is it art or doodling she does when she's
supposed to be doing something else – like work. Yeah, okay,
whatever. I guess doodling counts as art. Anyway, why are we
even having this discussion. I've got an assignment. I've only
been home from school about an hour, and already mom made
me feel guilty because she has to buy me a uniform for band
and you distracted me from doing my work. I need to find an
aggravation-free zone somewhere in this house, or I'll never

be the person I plan to be when I grow up. Oh, you wouldn't understand. No, no, no. My plan is for me to know and you to find out. When? (smiling, she says) Someday.

Annie's Acting and Babysitting Service Extraordinaire

I'm an entrepreneur. I know it's a very long word, but it just means that I have a business of my own. Yeah, I know I'm just a kid so it's very surprising, but not all that unusual, really. You just have to hang out with the right crowd to bump into a few more. Kid entrepreneurs that is. Kids with businesses. Don't worry, that's the last really long word I'll probably say for like, probably the rest of the day. My specialty isn't vocabulary. It's acting and babysitting. That's right. I like to act and I like to teach acting. And, I like to baby sit and I like to make money. So, I just rolled all those things into one and came up with my biz. That's short for business. Oh. You heard that one before. So, as I was saying, I'm the owner of Annie's Acting and Babysitting Service Extraordinaire. Oh, shoot! I guess I lied before when I said that I wasn't gonna say another long word, but – that was probably really the last one. I'm sure. So, anyway, that's my story and – so what else do you want to know for your article, kid? Well, you are writing an article aren't you? For the school paper? I thought that was why I was being interviewed. Oh, a vlog? Seriously? You're in first grade and you have a vlog? Why didn't you tell me so? I would have asked my mother to braid my hair! Well, it's all crazy and frizzy and – gosh do I look okay? Where are the cameras? Where are the lights? Where's the director's chair? Oh, you're just using your phone. Okay. Not very dramatic, but okay. So, should I start over with the stuff I already told you now that you're rolling? Oh. So, what do you want me to talk about? Oh, okay. (speaks dramatically and with a lot of added personality, now that she knows she's being filmed) Well, when I babysit, the agreement is that I'll teach the kids - the ones who can talk - a little bit about acting. So, let's say I've got one little squirt who's about five years old. I give them a real simple line like "I wanna go for ice-cream." Just about everybody can memorize that. Then, I tell them to say it like they're trying to get their mother to take 'em for ice-cream after they just had three teeth pulled and a shot in the you know where. So, the ones with talent, who really get it will go all sweet and sad, "I wanna go for ice-cream." They're usually really good at that. Then I say, now say it like you're a real bossy kid and you like to tell everybody what to do. Then they go, "I WANNA FOR GO FOR IIIICE-CREAM!." That one is pretty easy for them too. Kids are natural born actors, so my job is really pretty easy. And I make a fortune. I mean a regular baby sitter is probably gonna make half what I charge. But, hey, with my skillset? I'm worth it. – So that's it, right? Shouldn't you yell "CUT"? Or, "That's a wrap?" Or something? How did I look?

Life's Like That

I always, always, always wanted to be an actress. Since I was five years old. And, I always wanted to be in a play ever since Mrs. James took us to see You Can't Take it With You in the third grade. I loved it. I wanted to be the girl who thinks she's a ballerina and dances around all the time. The whole class liked the show. But for me, it was different. I didn't just like the show, I wanted to be in the show. So bad that even though I loved it, I hated it at the same time. It made me miserable because I wasn't up there doing that too. That's how much I wanted to be an actress. Bekah and I talked about it on the bus on the way home. I said, "Don't you wish you could have been in that play?" Bekah looked at me like I was nuts. "No. Why?" I didn't even bother to explain. I just said, "No reason" and looked out the window. I remember thinking, Bekah's the best, but she'll never understand. She likes soccer, and tennis, and she's great at those things, but me? I can't kick or hit a ball to save my life. But, I can act. I know I can. The funny thing is. And, you're gonna love this. You really will. Last year Mrs. Nodelman, our fourth-grade teacher, sent home a paper for our parents to sign. It said that a casting director was coming to school and would be looking for kids to be in a movie being filmed downtown. At first my mother didn't want to sign it because she's suspicious of everything. But, I begged like crazy and even cried. I think the crying worked, because she gave in. I gave the paper to Mrs. Nodelman, and the next day they called a bunch of us kids to go to the gym to meet this lady in a red dress. I was surprised to see that Bekah was there. She came up to me and said "This is dumb. My mother found out about this from Mrs. Nodelman and she made me come and audition." Well, you can probably see where this is going. When they made the announcement that Bekah got picked for the part it was all over school. And all over the internet. Turns out the movie they were making downtown was going to be super huge. That was a year ago, and I haven't seen Bekah much since then. I think she's being home schooled or going to some special school for famous kids. Well, she isn't famous yet, but my mother says she probably will be. She says the director of the movie is some famous wise-guy. I just keep thinking how it all isn't fair. Bekah didn't even want to go to the audition. She didn't even want to act. And that's all I ever wanted to do. I told my mother that I don't even want to see the movie. She acted all surprised and said I was jealous and made me cry. I tried to explain to her the unfairness of it all. I think she felt sorry for me for a minute. She looked kind of sad and said, "Life's like that. Now you know."

Funeral for a Friend

(Marsha stands in a black skirt and sweater with face turned up
to the sky. After a moment she looks at the audience). Robbie.
Robbie's funeral. So sad to say those words. Never thought
I'd have to go to a funeral for a friend. (looks down at her feet
then back to the audience) Robbie's gone, but I'm still here.
I'm. Still. (looks down at her feet again) Here. (looks back up
to the sky) I miss you, Robbie. I miss you already. (shaking her
head and looking around her) When I went to sleep last night I
prayed that I would wake up and this would all be a bad dream
and you would be here and we'd be together today, taking the
bus to the beach or hanging out, listening to music, just like any
normal Saturday. Just like it should be. I prayed so hard, but
when I woke up I knew. You're really gone. And Saturday or
any other day, will never be normal again. I always thought I
understood what death was. I mean we all know that everybody
has to die. But people are supposed to live long lives and get old
and they are not supposed to be killed walking across the street
in their own neighborhood. That is not supposed to happen.
And, I guess, I just never realized how death is so (searching
for the right word) final. You and I used to be able to help each
other out of any problem. Remember when I called you after
I lost my grandmother's wedding ring? I was supposed to drop
it off at the jewelers in the mall to have it resized, but I lost it
in the food court somewhere. You came to the mall and we
scoured the place. You even went through all the garbage cans.
Then I found it. In my pocket. You could have been so mad at
me, but you just laughed. You laughed so hard that you fell on

the ground and then I laughed so hard that I peed my pants. And then, forget about it. You couldn't stop laughing for an hour. You were the best friend Robbie that anybody ever had. (pause) So, it's your funeral today and I don't think I can go in there and do this. I wanted to stop here first and talk to you and see…if you could go in there with me? One last time? Be there for me? (looks up at the sky with tears in her eyes.) Thanks. (takes a breath and looks over to the right) Okay, Robbie. Let's do this together. (exits stage right with head held high)

The Wedding Dress

(Slouched in a chair, watching Rebecca try on clothes) You look good. I said, YOU. LOOK. GOOD. (with very little energy) Nooo, not just good. Great. You. Look. Great. I do mean it. Do too. I AM SAYING IT LIKE I MEAN IT! REBECCA! Come on, I'm getting tired of this. And I'm starving. Let's go to lunch. Two more dresses? Are you kidding? Well, I'm going to lunch. You can take pictures and send them to me. That is too, good enough. Why do you need my opinion anyway?! You know what looks good. I don't. Since when did you ever even respect my opinion on fashion? You're always making fun of what I wear. (repeating what she just heard with disbelief) My poor fashion choices are just because I'm poor?! Since when are you allowed to call me poor? Yeah, I know I say it all the time, but that's okay. I can do that. Cause I'm talking about me. You don't get to say that. Okay. Don't ever say that again. Okay. Okay. I'm sorry, too. (under her breath) I'm sorry I came here today. I said, I'M SORRY I CAME HERE TODAY! I don't care who's looking at me. (looks around) Go ahead and stare ya'll, whoever you are. (to Rebecca) You asked for my opin-ion, so here it is. My opinion is that this whole…THING… is ridiculous. This whole thing. You're taking this whole wedding way too seriously. You are not the one getting married. Your sister is! She's the one that everyone in the room is going to be staring at. NOT YOU! You are twelve years old. Nobody is even going to notice what you have on. They might not even notice that you're there. Is that what's bothering you? Is that why we're in this stupid store wasting a perfectly good day that could have been spent at the beach? You just can't stand the idea that all of the attention is going on Susan and there's zero attention on you. Yeah, of course, you hate me. I hate you right back. (sarcastically) Isn't that what friends are for? Oh, come on Rebecca! I take back everything I said. Can we please just go get something to eat? I'm starving!

The Domino Effect

Aunt Marina just kept saying, (imitating Aunt Marina's voice) "There wasn't a dry eye in the house." (crying in an exaggerated ridiculous way) "Oh, boo hooooo. Oh, ho, boo hoooo." (then grabs her sleeve and pretends to blow her nose in it) (imitating Aunt Marina again) "It was just beeyootiful!" Then my mom says, "Really? Two old geezers renewing their wedding vows after about a hundred years of a contentious marriage." Anyway, I'm pretty sure she said "contentious." Or, maybe she said "difficult." I don't remember exactly, but contentious is her favorite word. So, anyway, they got in a fight over it all and they're not talking to each other again. They have a contentious relationship. Oh no, it wasn't my grandparents renewing their vows. It was Aunt Marina's husband Fred's mother and father. Yeah, I met them twice. Once when I was born. I don't remember it very well, but I've seen pictures. And, then when Aunt Marina got married to Uncle Fred. I remember them pinching my cheeks a whole bunch and smelling like garlic. No, I didn't smell like garlic. They did. Obviously. I would never smell like garlic. You know why??? That's right. I hate garlic. See, you do pay attention occasionally. Just kidding. So anyway, that's why I said I couldn't sleep over tonight because of the domino effect. My mom is not talking to my Aunt Marina, so she's in a terrible mood, which is why I know she'll say no, that I can't sleep over. She'll probably want me to watch an old movie on tv tonight and then play scrabble till we're exhausted and can barely keep our eyelids open. So, basically, if you're gonna blame someone for me not coming over, you have to blame my Aunt Marina or actually probably Uncle Fred's parents. Don't worry. They'll make up. And, I'll probably be able to sleep over next weekend. Unless... my mother gets in a fight with my brother Peter, and then...Just Kidding!

The Secret

Shhh! (whispers) Walk softly. My grandmother's sleeping in the
next room. If she wakes up and catches me she'll kill me. Then
she'll tell my mother and she'll kill me all over again. It's over
here. (opens up a drawer and pulls out a photo album, then
nervously says) Shut the door. (Opens the book, and thumbs
through the pages, pauses and stares for a minute. Speaking
in a more normal voice.) There he is. That's my dad. Uh huh.
That was their wedding day. (turns the pages) And there he is
with me. When I was born. My mom doesn't want me to see
these…cause my dad left us when I was two and she never talks
about him. She doesn't want to talk about him. I've tried and
it's a really bad idea. I found these when we moved here last
year. She would die if she knew. (looks through the pages again)
Here's one of him in front of our old house. I loved that house.
Mom had it up for sale for years, and finally we got a buyer.
She said she never wanted to see that house again. She has really bad memories there. I wish I knew why he left, but I'm kind
of afraid it was because of me. Some people don't like babies
or kids, ya know. I mean, I'm not the easiest person to get along
with now, and I can just imagine what an awful baby I must
have been. That's probably why my mom won't talk about it.
She doesn't want me to know how much my dad couldn't stand
me. Maybe it isn't true. (pauses and decides to tell something
more) I'll tell you a secret if you swear that you'll never tell a
soul. Last week, I thought I saw him. My dad. I was coming out
of school and I looked across the street and he was just stand-
ing there at the bus stop, staring at me. I just stood there. Like

I was frozen. And then a huge truck passed between us and when it was gone, so was he. Why didn't I say something. Or do something? I don't know. Wave. Jump up and down. Anything! Yeah, (pauses to think) maybe it wasn't him. Yeah. Why would it be?

The Chocolate Milk Test

Some people want to be popular at school. Me? I just want one really good friend. And, since I move around a lot, I've found that sometimes one really good friend can be hard to find. It's like, someone might have a lot in common with me, but we just don't have that spark. That magic that happens when you meet someone and you both just get each other. Like, when something silly happens you both laugh until the chocolate milk you've been drinking at lunch comes out of your noses at the same time. Then you know. This is the one. That hasn't happened to me for a long, long, long time. And, I've tried. I really have. And, sometimes chocolate milk would be just streaming out of my nose, and I'd look over and…nothing. Not even a chuckle. And then there's other times when I'd look over and there's milk streaming down like the Victoria Falls, and I'd think, "Gee, that's not funny." Oh well. (sighs) So, I know that it can take weeks, or months, or years to find that one good friend. And, then, sometimes it happens in just a day. One day. Like yesterday. I got moved to Mrs. Grayson's class because Mr. Legend's class was too full. I was bummed, but it turned out to be the best thing ever. Mrs. Grayson gave me the seat right next to Suzzy and by the end of the day, we knew. Just one day, and I found one good friend. One friend who gets me. And that's all I need to be happy. Just one.

One Sheep, Two Sheep, Red Sheep, Blue Sheep

(Putting down a page and taking off her glasses) Well, little Lilly, you've had quite a summer haven't you. I've just finished the last story that you wrote. Yes, I liked it. I really did. I like them all so much. Gosh, this last one was awfully fun. (looks at the title page again) *One Sheep, Two Sheep, Red Sheep, Blue Sheep*. It reminds me of something else I read once (pretending to think hard) let's see, what was it? Oh yes, something by Dr. Suess. But yours was awfully good, Lilly. And the other story, the one you wrote about Christmas and that poor family, and the little boy with the crutches. (Pretending to think again) Let's see, what was his name? Oh, yes, *Tiny Tom*. It was a very sweet story. Reminds me just a little of something by Charles Dickens. And then, I just couldn't believe you wrote a novel! At your young age! I was very impressed. And such an interesting character, too. Scarlet O'Hana! And what was the name of your novel? Oh yes, *Gone with the Hurricane*! Now, how on earth did you ever think of that? And, then this last one. A movie script. My goodness. While all the other kids were out playing, somehow you came up with this clever story called... Ah yes, *Despicable You*. My goodness Lilly. You've put in so much work. It's just that... well, I love you so much, but I think these ideas remind me of things I've read or seen before. I know you want to be a writer like your friend Shelly and you can be. I know you can. It's just that you have to try harder to come up with your own ideas. Be original. Oh, don't cry. I know you can. Not only do I know you can, but I can't wait until you do. Your ideas will be so much better and more wonderful, because they will be all yours. And

Continued

no one is exactly like you.

Life with Father

I love him, and I hate him. How is that possible? I don't know how, but I know it is. Because I do. I love him because…he's my dad. And I know that he's had a hard life. He doesn't talk about it, but I know. Mom used to tell me about it. She used to explain everything away. Dad's always angry because that's all he knew growing up. I met my grandfather once and he… didn't even say my name. He didn't hug me, or really even look at me. He was…cruel. So, I feel sorry for my dad. My mom said that they got married because they loved each other and that my dad wanted a new start, but some how he just wasn't able to make one. I always felt like she was just making excuses. Maybe she was right. Maybe it's impossible for him to forget the past and be the father that I wish he could be. When mom was alive it was bad, but now it's worse. Once when he didn't know I was in the house, I heard him on the phone with his brother, my Uncle Tom. He was crying and he said he had nothing but regret for the way he treated mom. But that didn't change him. He drinks all the time now. He doesn't say a word to me unless he's criticizing me. For not cleaning up. For not being able to cook. For being in his way. I wish mom were here. I wish I didn't have to be afraid to come home from school every day. When I turn the corner to our street, if his truck isn't in the driveway, I'm glad. Sometimes that means he's working, and sometimes it means he's at a bar. With his friends. When Mom died Aunt Lou wanted me to come live with her, but he wouldn't even talk about it. He got so angry. I thought he didn't want me to go because he really did love me. But I know

Continued

now. That wasn't true. He doesn't love me. He thinks…I'm just something he owns. Like a spare tire. Not a very good one, but it will help him get by. So, Mom is gone, but he can still yell at me and boss me around and tell me what a jerk I am. It makes me want to scream. Don't you see? Don't you care? Don't you know what you're doing to me?

The Loneliest Girl in the World

There's a girl on my street. A girl who no one really knows.
She has a family and she has a lot of friends. The house is busy
and people all come in and out and people come and go. But,
although she smiles and seems to be content, there is no one
who really knows…this girl, or all the thoughts inside her head.
Inside her head and in her heart and soul. She will not tell
anyone how she feels because she's certain that they'd never understand. So deep, and deep, and deeper down she goes. Inside
herself where secrets swirl and dwell. And when you think she's
looking right at you, she's looking far away, inside her thoughts
and to another world. A world that she will never let you in.
It is her special power to deceive. When everyone around her
thinks they know just what she's like and who she wants to be.
But they don't know a single tiny thing. And they could never
guess or fathom who she is. She is the loneliest girl that you will
ever see. She has no one, and no one can have her. Not as a
friend, or sister, daughter or a niece. She will pretend, but it can
never be. How do I know? The loneliest girl is me.

The Noodle with the Poodle

He loves me! The boy with the red bike and the yellow hat! He loves me. Yeah, I know, I don't even know his name and he doesn't know mine. But he knows I exist. And he has a huge, tremendous, gorgeous crush on me. As big as a Super Moon, and maybe bigger. So, remember how I told you he used to make fun of Gloria, Alice and me? Every time he passed us when we were walking to the mini-mart he used to call us spaghetti noodles. Gloria hates him because he said we looked just like spaghetti noodles. Alice wasn't a fan either because she hates being skinny. My mom says she'll grow out of it. I say she looks beautiful and we all look beautiful just as we are. And we don't need to grow out of anything. I'm in a good place with who I am because I've spent a lot of time thinking about the things I like about myself and cultivating a healthy self-image. Anyway, I didn't mind being called a noodle. I thought it was kind of funny and that he was ridiculous, but cute. (sighs) I always fall for the ridiculous ones. And, of course, I was hoping that he was teasing us because he liked us and he was just too immature to express it appropriately. That's what my dad told me that boys do. I was, like, "Oh, dad! You're so smart!" But I was really thinking, duh! Girls do that too sometimes. Anyway, so yesterday was Valentine's day, right? Well, I came home and there was a cute little pink stuffed dog on the front porch with a card. Guess what it said? "Here's a Poodle for a Noodle!" I loved it! I mean, what's so bad about being a noodle? It's like Shakespeare said, "A rose by any other name..."

The Snaggle-Toothed Dragon

Okay. I wrote the script, so I should get to cast the characters, don't you think? That's how it works in the movies! Dad! Dad! I wrote the script for our puppet play, so I should get to decide who plays what, right? Wrong? Wrong? Are you sure? Okay. Okay. Lourdes you can be the casting director. Who gets to play the lead? Should we have auditions? I want to play the Snaggle-Toothed Dragon! Yeah, that's the main part – the lead. I wrote him, so I think I know him best. The other parts are the Princess, the Prince, and the kids. The Princess is a really good part because she's really pretty and needs to be rescued. Harper, I think you would be good for that. Just my opinion. Lourdes will of course make the final decision. Then there's the handsome Prince who she thinks is going to save her. That will have to be somebody who doesn't mind trying to sound like a boy. But, the twist is that the Prince doesn't really save her. The Princess thinks he's going to save her, but it's really the Snaggle-Toothed Dragon who saves her. Well, no really, she saves herself, but it's the Snaggle-Toothed Dragon who helps her to see how smart she is and gives her the courage to save herself. Yeah, the dragon. See he's a really nice dragon, but nobody knows it. Every time the kids are playing, he comes out to join them, but he looks kind of scary and he's like "Hey, let me play" in a big scary voice, so they all run away. So, there are some extra kid parts, but we can all play those. You know, just change our voices a little. Like "Oh, no, it's the dragon, help!" "Oh, no, it's the Snaggle-Toothed Dragon again!" So, yeah, it's kind of a sad story with a happy ending. The kids are

Continued

afraid of the dragon, but he keeps trying and he finally makes friends with the Princess, because she isn't just pretty. She's kind and compassionate and she notices when the Snaggle-Toothed Dragon looks all sad and cries when nobody wants to play with him. It's not like the other kids are mean, but they're afraid and they think of dragons as bad because that's what they learned in story books. So, the Princess is the only one who can think for herself, because she's had so much time alone in her tower to think. And, she's really good at it. So, the Snaggle-Toothed Dragon and the Princess become friends and he tells her she's so smart that she doesn't need the Prince to save her. She can easily save herself. It's a great story right?

Summer Sisters

(Talking on the phone) Wow! That's great news! You are? When? Really? Oh my gosh! Yeah! Well, okay. Bye. Yeah. Yeah. I'll...see you soon. (hangs up the phone) You'll never believe this. Monique is moving to Baltimore. Uh huh. Next week. Her parents bought the house down the street. I'm in total shock. Umm. Well, yeah. I guess I'm happy. I should be right? I mean, we're best friends at camp. We've known each other since first grade. It's just...we're Summer Sisters. Summer sisters. Not winter spring and fall sisters. I mean, we get along great at camp, but how will we get along in the real world. She's all excited because she's going to see me next week. Her BFF. Yeah, I am her BFF. In the summer. In my real life, Cameron is my BFF. And Monique and Cameron won't get along at all! They will be like oil and water. Monique is goofy, and Cameron is cool. All my friends at school are kind of...cool. We're cool. You know. What am I going to do? Make a choice? Between Monique and Cameron? Are you kidding? Uggh! I wish this were a dream. I...I...just have to let her know. This is my real life. You can't just drop into it and expect everything to be like it is at camp. Summer is summer and life is life. And Summer Sisters aren't really sisters after all.

To Be Me

If they knew what's it like to be me, I wonder if they'd be as cruel and mean. Do they know what it's like to wake up to the sound of fighting every night? I do. Do they know what it's like to feel like no one in the world loves you? I do. Do they know what it's like to come home one day and find out that your stuff has been packed and you're being sent away? "For your own good?" I do. So, maybe I don't act like all the other kids. Maybe that's because I'm not. I'm not anything like them and they're not anything like me. They know I'm different because I'm trouble. I'm the one with no friends. The girl who always does the wrong thing at the wrong time, says the wrong thing, and says it too loud. I'm the girl who looks the wrong way, at the wrong person! I'm the one nobody likes, and nobody wants, and nobody ever will! Sure, they know who I am, but do they know why? If they did, would they care? If they knew, what would they do? Something? Anything? Nothing? Or would they wish me away, just like everyone else? Like a bad dream. I wonder.

The Doll House

(Kneeling at a gravesite) Hello Dad, it's me Violet. I brought you flowers. They were mom's favorite, so I knew you'd like them too. You always thought she was so smart. I miss mom. I miss you. Charlotte's taking good care of me. You were right. Remember? When you got re-married, after mom died. Remember? You said, "If anything ever happens to me, I know Charlotte will take care of you." She has. She does. She drives me to school every morning, so I don't have to take the bus. She bought me a bunch of clothes for school this year. She doesn't like to go pick them out together like you and I did, or mom and me. But, I don't mind. It wouldn't be the same anyway. But she gave me money and let me go with Christine and her mom. They're the people who live next door. The new house is pretty nice. It's smaller and Charlotte says it will help her to make ends meet. Anyway, I only have a few minutes and then the bus will be here, and I need to be on it. Charlotte thinks I'm at the library. I'll be in trouble if she finds out I came here on my own. It's just…I wanted to tell you about the doll house. You know how I loved it. I still remember when you made it for me. It was supposed to be a surprise, but I ran into the garage to tell you that dinner was ready, and I saw it before you could cover it up. It was so beautiful. I loved it so much. I still do. But, it's only a memory now. There wasn't room for it in the new house. Everything that we didn't need had to go. I cried, and Charlotte got mad. She said it was wrong of me to try to make her feel worse than she already feels. I just don't know why I had to get rid of my doll house and Glenn got to keep his surfboard. I

Continued

guess I'm feeling a little like Cinderella these days. Maybe one day I'll meet a Prince Charming and we'll live in a beautiful palace. Or maybe a house as beautiful as the one you built for me. I love you Dad. The bus is here. I love you Dad. Goodbye.

Herbie Illman's Magic Spell

I'm so sleepy. I know I said I'd go, but for some reason I'm sooo
tired. Do you think I could just lay down here on the sidewalk
for about…an hour. (yawns) Oh look, how about that spot of
grass under that big oak tree. Yes, I know we only have one
hour. We have to get the magic lantern to the house on the
hill before the sun goes down or your wish won't come true
and Donny Parket won't always love you forever and ever till
(yawns) the end of (nods off momentarily and wakes up when
her chin drops) time. I'm sorry, but you'll have to go on without
me. I don't know what's wrong with me. I must have eaten too
much Valentine's candy. This is terrible. Now I won't be able to
go with you to the house on the hill and I won't be able to go
to the dance tonight with Jaime. Oh my gosh. That's it. I won't
be able to go to the Valentine's dance with Jaime. Remember
this afternoon when I opened Herbie Illman's Valentine? It said
"I love you and I don't want you to dance with anyone else but
me." Remember? That's it. Herbie Illman gave you the magic
lantern. He must have used it last night to put a spell on me
so that I'd be too sleepy to go the dance with (yawns) Jaime.
You've got to help me Margo. You've got to help me get home,
so I can get dressed and go to the dance with Jaime, even if I
have to sleep walk, or sleep dance. I'm going to (yawns) get to
the dance with Jaime and nothing, not even Herbie Illman is
going to stop me.

My Life, The Musical

My life is a musical from morning to night. My mother wakes me up by singing an obnoxious song about Freddy the Clown that drives me nuts. It's worse than an alarm clock. Then, when she's making me pancakes she makes up songs about the beautiful day ahead and my dad chimes in. They giggle and cuddle over the pancakes while I growl and groan. Beautiful day?! I have to face the most irritating, demanding, demoralizing teacher in the whole school who starts each morning with a pop quiz and likes to call us by our seat number instead of our name. But I never complain to my parents. I did once and they looked at each other for about one minute and then started singing some dreary song from an Opera they sang in together in college by some guy named Wagner. It lasted about an hour and by the time they were finished I had taken my shower, jumped in bed and pulled the covers over my head. I don't think they were even aware that I'd left the room. It's crazy. I used to like music. I used to like my parents. I mean, everyone else in the whole world seems to think they're "soooo cute." But it's hard. It's a lot harder than you'd think, when your life is a musical where everything gets turned into a song. My friend Alice and I were walking down the hall at school and as we passed the chorus class, Alice pointed to it and said, "If you can't beat 'em, join 'em." I rolled my eyes so hard, I think I almost sprained my eye sockets. I said, "You're right." I walked in and signed up for after-school chorus and I start next week. When I told my parents, well…you guessed it! They were so happy… broke into song.

A Month Away from Home

When my mother first told me I'd have to go live with the Wiesmans in Utah for a month because she had to go to Europe for work, I cried. And cried. And cried. I think I cried for about three days straight. It seemed like the end of the world to me, leaving New York City and our apartment. I've never been away from my mother for more than a week, and usually someone comes to stay with me. Like Nana Carol, or Mrs. Bumstock. And sometimes mom has taken me with her. I got to go to Chicago that time she had to deliver a speech. It was exciting and fun and we saw all sorts of sights and had the best hot dogs in the universe. I couldn't understand why she wouldn't take me with her to Europe. I want to see Paris. I want to see Rome. I knew I wouldn't get in the way. But it wasn't "up for discussion." So, I packed my bags and went on my first plane trip alone to go stay with the Wiesmans, mom's "oldest and dearest friends" who I've never even met. The flight attendants were super nice, but they kept talking to me like I was about three. One even asked me if I had a teddy bear or special blanket with me. I was like, "no thank you, I'll just enjoy reading. I'm in the middle of Dostoevesky's Crime and Punishment on my e-reader and I can't wait to see how it ends." She just looked at me like I was speaking in another language and didn't bother me for the rest of the flight, which was a relief because I wasn't in the mood. I felt like I was being punished, and like just being a kid was my only crime. I just kept thinking, why should I be sent away from the comforts of my home, or excluded from a European adventure because I buy my clothes in the kids' de-

Continued

partment? By the time the plane landed I had come up with a plan. I was going to wear a permanent scowl on my face for 30 days, and answer "yes, ma'am" and "no, ma'am" and nothing more. I would keep my nose in a book and refuse to participate in anything the old Weismans had planned. But, then, when I got off the plane and saw the Wiesmans, I felt myself smile a smile so big it made my face hurt. The Wiesmans had brought their whole family to the airport to greet me. Including their twin sons, William and Sam who are exactly my age. And, even though they're identical, I kept trying to decide which one was cuter. That month went by so fast that I wasn't ready to leave when it was over. My mom came to pick me up and fly home with me. The night before we left, I cried. And cried. And cried. I knew I'd miss the Weismans and all the fun we had during my month away from home.

Dear Uncle Jimmy

When I can't sleep, I like to write a letter to an imaginary uncle, Uncle Jimmy. Well, he's not entirely imaginary. I remember my mother watching a famous writer on her computer. His last name was James and he kept telling her, well everyone who was watching, how they could be rich just like him. I thought it sounded wonderful and I imagined how wonderful it would be if he weren't just some writer that we didn't know. I imagined that he might be a friend of my mother's, or a relative, like my uncle. I imagined, if he were my uncle, and he knew all the problems we were having, and all the things we needed, that we couldn't afford, I could just write to him and he would send money right away. And he even might send for us and let us stay in his magnificent house in Florida, with the swimming pool and the view of the Atlantic Ocean. I imagined how wonderful that would be. I imagined how safe I would feel knowing that I was special to him and that he loved me. My Uncle Jimmy. That's what I called him. I would write these wonderful letters that told him all about how I was doing in school and that I hadn't told the other kids about him because I didn't want to brag. I'd write that I was planning a wonderful vacation to stay with him and his wife. I called her Aunt Louise. I wrote that I knew she would want to buy me new outfits when I got there, and, of course, take me for my nails and hair. They were wonderful letters, and as silly as it sounds, they helped me to go back to sleep at night. Of course, I never mailed them. He's not my Uncle Jimmy and he doesn't even know who I am. But, it would be wonderful if he was my uncle. Wouldn't it? I

Continued

wonder if he actually has a niece in real life, and if he loves her the way I imagine he would love me. I wonder, if he knew there were two people in this world that he could help so easily, if he would care. I imagine he would.

My Favorite Memory

Kristy's crying again, and she won't let me in her room. It's so frustrating. This happens all the time. She thinks we don't love her. That no one likes her. It all started with that jerk who stood her up for the Junior Prom. Donny Musterluck. I know, right! Who would have ever imagined that Donny Musterluck could send anybody off the deep end? (sighs) But, why on earth does she think I don't care? I mean, I tried to tell her that she would have a million more dates and that Donny was a jerk. She said that I didn't take her problems seriously and that I was "trivializing" and making fun of her love for Donny. "Just like everyone else." I can't believe she would do that! Lump me in with everyone else. I mean, we're not just sisters, we're friends. We always say that! I always mean it, too! Why doesn't she believe me anymore? If she'd let me in her room, I'd try to convince her again, but I'm not sure it would work. I've tried about a thousand times already. I even wrote a poem for her. I'll read it to you. It's called, "My Favorite Memory is You" (clears throat before reading)
"Roses are red, Violets are blue
I tried to remember my favorite time and for some strange reason I only saw you.
I only saw you because you were always there,
When I laughed, when I cried, when I hadn't a care.
If someone would ask for my favorite things, I'm sure I'd come up with a nice thing or two.
But for my favorite memory, without a doubt it's always been you." The End. What do you think? Thanks! I thought it was

Continued

good too. (shakes her head in disbelief) When I read it to Kristy, she just started wailing and calling out Donny's name. You know, I definitely liked her better before puberty.

I'm Just a Girl

I'm just a girl…who wants to save the world. I'm just a girl … with a dream as big as that mountain. I'm just a girl…with a heart as big as that ocean and as pure as the gold in your shiniest ring. I'm just a girl…who is more valuable than that huge, gigantic, much-too-large diamond on her lovely left hand. Why? Why you may ask am I so valuable? Because I want to change the world…for the better. I want to help people. All people. Because they matter. I will reach down and pull you up. I will reach out and pull you in. If you give me a chance. If you're there for me. If you do what you should and bring me up right. Teach me what I need to know. Build up my confidence, don't break my self-esteem. Tell me I can do anything! Don't tear me down! Tell me I can work hard and make my dreams come true. Tell me that you'll look out for me when I need you, and you can see good things for me as I grow older, because you know. You can see. I'm going places. I'm going to rock your world, and his world, and her world, and our world. I'm just a girl. And that's a wonderful thing to be.

On the Phone with Tara

(yelling) You're not my mother, so stop acting like that!! (to the phone) My sister is driving me crazy. Just because my mom is basically never here anymore...she's working two jobs now. Yeah, at the hospital and some real estate office. Uh huh. So, yeah, just because my mom is, like never here anymore, Jennifer thinks she's in charge of everything, including me. I mean, she is in charge, but only, like, in an emergency. You know, like if I fell and broke my head open or something, she should call 911 or drive me to the hospital or something. Oh. My. Gosh! She thinks she's in charge of telling me when to breathe, when to sit, when to stand, when to do my homework, when to go to bed. Seriously! Well, I wasn't serious about the breathing or sitting part. No. Um. No. Wow! You're really gullible. Gullible. G.U.L.L.I.B.L.E. You don't know what gullible means? You need to improve your vocabulary girl! It means you'll believe anything. Whatever! So, anyway, what happened when you told Jimmy Hendrix that you like him. He did not! No way!! You have got to be kidding! What? Oh, you are kidding. Um. No, I am not gullible. No. That could totally have happened. So, he didn't say that? What did he say? You didn't tell him? What? Girl! When are you going to tell that dude what's on your mind. (hears Jennifer calling) Hold on. (yelling) What?!!! (to the phone) Oh, my gosh! My mom's home. I gotta go. No. I gotta go. Talk to you tomorrow Tara. (jumps up with a smile) Mom!

The Curious Case of the Snotty-Rottens

(While babysitting, Miriam settles the children down to tell them a little bedtime story.) Okay, tonight for story time I'm going to tell you the story about a sweet little girl named Emma. Emma was a very good girl, almost all the time. She woke up with a smile on her face, said good morning to her mommy and daddy, and gave them a kiss each day. She ate all of her breakfast. Then she carried her plate and her cup to the sink like a big girl. She helped her little brother find his pacifier at least ten times a day, and she even fed her pet Hannah, the hamster, on time, so that Hannah didn't get too hungry and faint like her big brother's gerbil once did. She never cried when her parents went out to parties and she always, ALWAYS, minded her manners and behaved for her babysitter. She went to bed when she was told, and she never ever, ever complained. Emma was basically a very, very good little girl. But one day something very strange happened. It was not only strange, it was peculiar. Yes, peculiar. One day, sweet, dear, little Emma woke up – (GASP) – without a smile on her face. And where she usually had a smile, she wore the most unusually bad-tempered frown. In fact, you could say it was the frowniest frown in all of the town. Yes, the frowniest frown. When Emma woke up with her frowny-frown she refused to say good morning to her mommy, and that made her mommy cry. She refused to say good morning to her daddy, and that made her daddy sigh. She didn't even give them a kiss, and instead of eating her breakfast she cried, "I want cookies!" Well, needless to say, the rest of the day only got worse. Emma's little brother cried all day because he kept losing his pacifier,

Continued

and nobody helped him to find it. Hannah, the hamster, didn't get fed on time, and she got so hungry she almost fainted. And at the end of the day, Emma's babysitter got very, very upset indeed. Yes, indeed. You see, when the babysitter asked Emma to go to bed, she didn't listen at all. She whined, and cried, and complained, and ran around the house in her pajamas throwing a tantrum. This made her babysitter cry at first. But then, she got an idea. The babysitter thought, Emma isn't herself today. She must be sick. I'll call the doctor. Yes, the doctor. And she did. She called the doctor and he came over right away. Well, when the babysitter told the doctor what was wrong with Emma he was pretty certain he knew what was wrong. He said, "My dear, have no fear, it sounds like dear sweet little Emma has caught something that's been going around in this neighborhood. Yes, it sounds like dear Emma has a serious case of the Snotty-Rottens. "The Snotty-Rottens?" the babysitter asked. "Yes, my dear, the Snotty-Rottens. And I have just the thing to make them go away. Hmmm," he said, "Let's see, it's in my bag somewhere. Here it is. My giant needle for the Snotty-Rotten shot." "Oh, dear," the babysitter said, "Emma won't like getting a shot." "Well," the doctor said, "Tell Emma that sometimes if the patient gets into bed right away and goes to sleep, the Snotty-Rottens will go away on their own. Let her give that a try and see if it works. If not, call me back right away." So, the babysitter told Emma, and Emma, being a very smart little girl who didn't like shots, got into bed and counted sheep until she went soundly to sleep. And in the morning,

Emma was back to her old sweet self again. The curious case of the Snotty-Rottens had gone away to stay. Well, at least until another day.

Honest Feedback

My friend, Caroline, had Imelda call me while they were both
on the line, only I didn't know it, Imelda asked questions and
tried to get me to agree that Caroline was essentially a jerk. I
was like, "No way, Caroline is one of my best friends. When
I moved here, she took me under her wing. She may not be
perfect, but nobody is. I would never trash talk my bestie."
Well, as soon as I said that I heard giggling on the phone and
I recognized that giggle. I couldn't believe it. It was Caroline.
She had been listening the whole time. She got on the phone
still laughing and told me she had to see if I was loyal and, hey,
how awesome…I had passed the test. I was stunned. I was literally speechless. I felt so betrayed. I just stood there for a minute staring at the phone. Then I hung up. Caroline texted me
and said she had to do it because she had to know how good
a friend I was. I didn't respond for a whole day and she kept
texting and saying I was being a baby and how I should forgive
her and get over it. After all, she was one of the most popular
girls in school, she said, and she couldn't waste her time being
friends with just anybody. I said I forgave her, but I wouldn't
forget, and I gave her some honest feedback.
I told her she could be dishonest and deceitful all she wants, but
she can't be that way with me. And, I told her that I honestly
felt she and Imelda had acted like a couple of total jerks.
Caroline tried to defend herself and said "If I'm such a jerk,
why do I have so many friends at school? You have to admit,
I'm more popular than you!" I thought about that for a minute
and then I wrote back. "Maybe you're like Limburger Cheese. I

mean, a lot of people like it, but it still stinks." I thought it was a great analogy, and I think expressing myself to her was really cathartic for me. I hope it was helpful for her as well. I think she really did need a little honest feedback. And wasn't that what she wanted in the first place?

Lost in Space

It didn't go well. I said, IT DIDN'T GO WELL!! I'm not shouting at you. I'm sorry. I'm just tired.

Every time I get back from spending the weekend with dad you ask me the same question, and every time, I have the same answer. Why do you keep asking? Why do you care? Really? You're asking because you care about me? It seems to me like you're glad it didn't go well. I'm sorry. I shouldn't have said that. But, if you really want to know how it went, why don't you ask dad. Yeah, I know. You're not talking to dad and he's not talking to you. But, when I come back from seeing him, you quiz me. When I get in the car to go with him, he quizzes me. You both just love to put me in the middle. And lately, I'm miserable around both of you. I feel like I don't belong anywhere. You're here, and he's there, and I'm…lost in space. I don't want to do this anymore. I want to go live with grandma. Why does that make you so mad? Why can't you even talk about it. Okay, fine, I'll go to my room. Great! That's where I was going when I came in the door. BEFORE YOU STOPPED ME! Fine, I'm grounded! FOR WHAT? Oh, who cares. I'm going. I'm going. You know what? I hope aliens come down in their spaceship tonight and take me to Mars. Then, you'll wish you let me go to grandmas. Fine, I'm going, I'm going, but if you don't see me tomorrow you'll know what happened. You'll know I went with the aliens. Maybe you can hire someone to go tell dad.

Love is an Action Verb

Hello and welcome to my Holiday vlog. Or, for those of you who have watched before, welcome back. So, I like to come up with fun things for the holidays, usually crafty type things and share them with you. Some of you may have tuned in for my first vlog on Halloween last year. We made some scary masks out of paper bags. And, then on Thanksgiving, I actually made a special Pilgrims' Corn and Pumpkin S'more dessert, which was a pretty big success in my house at the kids' table. If you made it along with me, and If it didn't give you too much of a belly ache, maybe you tuned in again at Christmas for my mix-it up Reindeer Dance Party ideas. (dances around for a bit singing Rudolph the Red-Nosed Reindeer and then laughs) That was a blast. And, now here we are approaching the big V-day. That is, Valentines. And, this Valentine's day I'm making my own Valentine cards. That's right, I'm giving all homemade - nothing store bought. As you can see in front of me, I'm using some awesome quotes about love that I found on the internet (holds up a piece of paper with some quotes on it), some red construction paper (waving hand over the paper), and some glitter and glue. I've already made about five of them and it's been so much fun! I can't believe I didn't do this before. So, we're going to make one together, but this time, I'm not going to use one of my internet quotes. Instead I'm going to use something my Sunday School teacher once said to me that really stuck with me. We were talking about Love and Mrs. Simmons sat there and looked at us all with this serious expression and said, "You know, love is an action verb." I think, at first, we just looked at her and thought, "so…?" And then she went on to say that if we love our neighbor, if we love our parents, if we love our friends and teachers at school, we should do things that reflect that love. We should take action to show that we care. So, enough of my lecture, as I'm sure you get the point. So now, I'm going to make a few Valentines with that quote from Mrs. Simmons on them. I'll use this red heart that I already cut out before I started filming. (starts to write and then looks up) Oh gosh, are you still there? You don't need to sit around and watch me do this. Remember? Love is an Action Verb. So, go take action! Happy Valentine's Day! From me to you.

Sometimes It's Crazy Being Me

Look at them. Over there. They're all in a circle playing party games. For my birthday. I had to excuse myself for a moment or two. I wish I could call a cab and excuse myself forever! This has been the most embarrassing week. It all started last weekend when I couldn't sleep because I was so excited about my birthday party. I was so excited because I had finally gotten up the nerve to invite Tommy Hall and amazingly enough, Tommy Hall had RSVP'd "Yes!" Yes! OMG! I was in a dream, only I wasn't in a dream, because I couldn't catch a wink. My mom and dad found that hard to believe. "Kids don't get insomnia," my dad said. "What in the world could you possibly be worrying about," mom chimed in brilliantly. I wasn't worried. Not really. I was excited. But, well, maybe worried and excited are close cousins. Do ya think? Anyway, as it turned out, I had plenty to worry about. Cause not-sleeping, being sleep-deprived that is, made me do really stupid things. Really stupid things! Like Monday morning. I got to the bus stop early so that I could have time to chat up Tommy Hall as soon as he arrived. He was an early bird and liked to sit on the bench and do the homework he hadn't done the night before. So, I got there SU-PER EARLY, so I could make sure I got the space on the bench beside him. So, there I sat in my new white pants and pretty white fake fur jacket, my lip gloss on, my favorite earrings - shaped like hearts with a dolphin jumping through them, and my ID bracelet engraved with the words "Peace, Laughter, and Love." I looked adorable! As I waited, I imagined Tommy arriving. He'd get out of his mother's car and say, "Good morning Adriana." Ah, the sound of Tommy Hall saying my name. In my imagination it sounded like music wafting down from heaven. I looked at the time and it looked like Tommy was late. I closed my eyes and imagined it again. "Good morning Adriana." And again. "Good morning Adriana." And each time it sounded better than the last. Finally, I heard a car pull up. I opened my eyes just as the car door opened and Tommy popped out, just like my morning waffle, all warm and toasty. He looked like he was thinking of something else and didn't see me at all. He didn't even head toward the bench! What happened? Did he do his homework last night? As he headed the other direction, I knew if we were going to chat, it would have to be up to me. I got up off the bench and stumbled in his direction, tripped over a branch and landed in a big patch of mud. That made him notice me! He looked over and I let out a goofy laugh to show that I was okay. And, then, it happened. I looked over at Tommy with stars in my eyes, and I heard the strangest words coming out of my own mouth. "Good morning Adriana," I said. Really, really LOUD! Tommy looked confused and embarrassed for me. He could have at least helped me up! But, he didn't. I started desperately wishing that my patch of mud was a sink hole, so I could disappear quietly. I didn't say another word and neither did he. I just rode to school all stained with brown mud on my pretty white jacket and new pants, wondering what I ever saw in Tommy Hall to begin with. Uggh! Sometimes it's crazy being me!

My Dream

So, what's yours? Your dream, silly! Of course you do! Everyone has a dream, don't they? Mine? Oh, that's easy. I actually
have lots of dreams. That's my favorite hobby you know, day
dreaming. The one Mrs. Reddy calls me out on, just about
every day, during Math. Yeah, I have a favorite dream. There's
one dream that I dream even more than I dream about Jason
Ovaltine. I dream of living in a big house with a swimming
pool. I'm getting tired of apartment life. I have one particular
house in mind. It's that beautiful big white house by the dog
beach! Uh huh. The one we pass on the way to Boyd's Burger
and Bacon Basement. When we move there, in my dream of
course, my dad is going to let me get a dog. I'm thinking of a
Swiss Doodle. Have you seen one? Oh, they're beautiful. And
when they're puppies! Oh, my gosh, soooo cute. They're hypo-
allergenic you know! That's right. So, even I can have one! Oh,
yeah, it's a great dream! In my dream, Pepper, that's my Swiss
Doodle, and I will go for a walk every morning and every night,
and she'll play in the surf and sand. We'll be so happy! And on
one of our walks just as the sun's going down, well, that's when
we'll just happen to bump into Jason Ovaltine. Now, won't that
be convenient.

The Last Laugh

Every Sunday, I dread Monday. Uggh! School! Again. If I only had one more day! One more little slice of the weekend! It's like desert after a long week of meat and potatoes. And it goes by too fast. The weekend that is, not the week. The week goes by like a snail, or a turtle or my sister Carol when she's doing the dishes. Uggh, uggh, uggh!! Not again. Not another week of homework. When is the next holiday anyway? I don't think I can make it that long. Maybe it's me? Maybe it's my attitude? Yeah, maybe. Or maybe it's Mrs. Battleby? No, I'm NOT making that up. My teacher's name is Mrs. Battleby. And, no, I do not call her Mrs. Battleaxe like the other kids. I haven't sunk that low. But, I admit that I did chuckle a few times. Is that so wrong? I mean, really? Don't they say that laughter is the best medicine. I know, I know, not when it's at someone else's expense. I don't know though. I read an article recently – yes, I do read! Anyway, I read an article recently that said that laughter is good for you, even if it's fake laughter. It said that there are some people who get together just to laugh at nothing. It does great things for their health. You know, just ha ha hawing over absolutely nothing. You want to try it? Come on. I'll go first. (starts laughing) See, it's not that hard. Now you. Okay, I'll do it with you. (starts laughing again) Hey, that was pretty good. I should do this Monday mornings as soon as I wake up. Maybe it would make me feel better about going to school. Or... (getting bright idea) maybe my mom will think I've lost it and let me stay home! Now that would be funny!

Built-in Babysitter

I'm getting tired of hearing that. You didn't hear what my mom's friend Betty just called me? A built-in babysitter. And you know what? She's right on the money, That is exactly what I am. And I don't like it. Of course I love my brother and sister, but…there are days…And why should I be the one who has to take care of them. Didn't my mom and dad sign up for that when they said, "I do" and then, started feathering their nest? You know, speaking of nests, I'd like to see a mommy or daddy Robin Red Breast make their teenager stay at home with the baby birds while they go out to gather worms. I don't think that ever happens. Well, no, I don't really know, but I'm pretty sure it doesn't. I mean, after Robby and Chrissy were born, at first it wasn't so bad. I was kind of flattered. You know, that my mom and dad trusted me with their most precious treasures. But that got old really fast. And now, quite frankly, I think they are taking advantage. Mom works late just about every night, and dad has all sorts of meetings to go to that I think he could do on the phone. He used to do them on the phone. Am I being paranoid? Am I just making assumptions? Maybe they really are doing the best they can. And, they do pay me. Sometimes. I mean, sometimes they just buy me stuff or let me go ice-skating and give me money. They did let me pick out the new paint for my room. Any color. (sighs) I don't know. It's a dilemma. Do I get mad and say, "No more?" I'm not sure if that would get me anywhere. No, I don't think I really have a choice. You know how it is. I mean, we're kind of an all for one and one for all family, and right now, I think that means I need to be the baby-sitter. I guess that's just how the cookie crumbled.

Wonder Girl

I was reading my old diary the other day. Reading it made me remember a lot of things. Like, for instance, my mom used to call me Wonder Girl. I would always come up with dreams of a better world. Like at my birthday party once, I blew out the candles and then I looked around the room and said, "I wonder what it would be like to live in a world where no one was homeless. Where no one was hungry. Where no one had to worry about being bullied when they got to school every morning. A world where everyone knew there was somebody who cared." My mom said I got that way of thinking from my grandmother. She was an activist and an idealist and a thinker. I always knew I was a thinker and an idealist and I wanted to be an activist too when I grew up. I wanted to try to find out what my ideal world, my dream world, would be like. But my dad always said, "Soon you'll get boy crazy like your sister Darleen and you won't wonder so much about the world." He said, "You'll wonder, why doesn't Johnny ask me to the dance? Or, what should I wear today to make Henry notice me." I thought my dad didn't know me very well. In one of my journal entries I said, "Dad, I'll prove you wrong! You'll see!!" It made me sad to realize that he was right. Funny, how it is when you look back after a few years and see your old self and wonder. What happened to the girl I used to be?

Things Change

Hmm? My bicycle? Oh. Dad sold it. Uh huh. No. I didn't. I didn't' get a new one. Just sold it. Well, it was my idea really. I think so anyway. Yeah, it was my idea. I don't really need a bicycle. Freddy lets me borrow his occasionally. And I'm so busy now that baby's here. Helping mother. I did love it. I did. I felt sad to see it go. But, it went to a really nice little girl. Over in Harsdale. Her Granddaddy picked it up for her, and the little girl came along. It was nice to see her so happy. Just like I was when I got it. I was just about her age, too. It made me feel good to see her with my bicycle. It was like, when we had to give Sammy away because he barked too much. I cried. But then I saw the family who got him. They were nice. And I could tell that they loved him right away. A dog should have a good family. And a bike should have a good home too. With someone who can ride it. Every day. I'm older now. Things change. I have responsibilities. I can't be…I don't know. Running around so much. Just having fun. There's a lot to do in the house. Mom and Dad expect…things from me. And that's good. I wouldn't want to be like you. To have it so easy. So, you see? You shouldn't feel sorry for me. I feel sorry for you. Your parents treat you like a baby. Yes, that's right a baby. Still playing games and having fun, while the real world is going on all around you. You don't need to get mad. I'm not saying anything that isn't true. Well, you can be mad if you want to. I guess I just don't see how we can be friends anymore anyway. Do you? I mean. I have things to do. You don't. And, no. I can't go riding today. To answer your question. I don't want to go riding. Or anywhere else. Ever again. Please don't ask me anymore.

My Dad the Cat – Well Sort Of

We're going to see the play tonight. I'm scared. No. Scratch that. I'm terrified. WHAT IF IT'S GOOD? Katrina! What if it's a hit?!! That means my dad will be playing a cat for…who knows how long. A year? Two years? A hundred? Of course, I'm exaggerating! But, I'm not exaggerating the issue. I mean, prepping for the audition was bad enough. My dad logged over 500 hours of watching cat videos in just one month. I know that doesn't sound humanly possible. That's what I said to my dad. You know what he said? "Well, it's cat possible!" Then he meowed and licked his hand. I'm serious. The rehearsal period was even worse. My dad picked me up from school wearing cat whiskers and a tail. It was embarrassing. No. It's wasn't just embarrassing, it was mortifying. Now, with the show opening tonight, I have a feeling all of this could last…forever. Oh, Katrina, Karina, Kabina, my dear, sweet best friend. Keep your fingers crossed for me. Let this show flop. Let it open and close in one night. Or (sighs) I could be eating tuna fish for the rest of my life.

She Said, Yawning

I got in trouble in Mrs. Schlitz's class again today. I fell asleep. Yup. And, it wasn't the first time. Yes, it's happened before. I didn't tell you because I was embarrassed. Three times. Uh huh. Mrs. Schlitz was furious. She got all red in the face and I think I saw steam coming out of her ears. It's not funny. She's going to call mom. I think. Well, she said she was going to call mom after the second time and she didn't, so I'm keeping my fingers crossed. I figure she probably has better things to do in her spare time than call mom. Plus, I told her that mom is working two jobs and if she wants to speak to her in person she'll have to call after 11 PM. She looked kind of funny when I said that. I think she felt sorry. Not for me. For mom. But she didn't say that. She just said, "Well, tell her I'll be calling then. After 11 PM. This week." I think she added "this week" cause she wasn't sure she could stay up after 11 tonight. She looked exhausted. Too many late nights grading papers, I guess. Anyway, I'm hoping she gets too tired to stay up any night this week and never calls. And, I hope I don't fall asleep in her class again! Well, I couldn't help it. I mean, I stay up every night until mom gets home because it's the only time I get to talk to her. I couldn't tell Mrs. Schlitz that! She wouldn't understand. Would she?

Myrtle the Diva Turtle

Excuse me, I think we need a spotlight over here. Yeah, over here. Yes, Sir Director Sir, I said something. It's me. Daniella Delores Darvinski. Over here in the dark. Yes, yes, that's right, under the tree, upstage of the rock, wearing a giant turtle costume. Yes, hi Mr. Director. I'm in here and I'm sorry to interrupt, but as an actress I just think my character wouldn't put up with this. Who am I playing? (aside) Gee whiz, if you don't know then we're in real trouble. (loudly) I'm playing Myrtle, sir. Yes, that's right. Myrtle the Turtle. And, I've done a lot of research and I'm studying the method with my coach on the weekends, and I think I know Myrtle pretty well by now, and she would never stand for this. This being stuck behind a rock, under a tree in the dark. She would definitely want to be in the spotlight sir. And, she'd also, pardon me for saying so, but she would definitely have a lot more to say. Well, Myrtle only has one line sir. I mean, give me a break. What's that sir? Oh, no, I'm not being disrespectful, sir. That's Myrtle's line. "Give me a break." Yes, sir. She says that after the tree branch, well, I mean just before the tree branch breaks off and falls on her head. Yes, sir, I know that's supposed to be funny. Yes, sir, I know it's important. A light moment in this dark, dark play about the environment. But, I just think Myrtle's got more going on for her than that. For instance, you may not know this, but Myrtle has a terrific smile and she's extremely friendly. So, it's just totally out of character that she would be on stage for two acts and stay in the same place and utter that one line. Hilariously funny though it may be. What? What do I think she should do? Well,

she might sing sir, or she might dance. I mean I see Myrtle sort
of grooving like this and then sort of fa la laing every now and
then. See, it's moving towards the Christmas season and Myrtle
has always been fond of the holidays. No, sir. You are correct.
That is not in the script. That's in Myrtle's back story. Yes, sir.
The one I made up. See, Myrtle has an awesome voice, but her
mother used to make her feel like she couldn't sing and then
one Christmas she didn't get any presents, but none of this even
phased Myrtle because she has something better than a thick
skin. She has a really hard shell. So, she just sings and gets excited about the holidays, and…yes, sir. I see. I will sir. I will. I'll
try to put all of that back story into my one line. Uh huh. Yup.
Give me a break! (aside) And that's not Myrtle talking.

When I Grow Up

What do you mean I'm not funny? So? I said I wanna be a comedian when I grow up. Hello! I know you're hearing me, but are you listening? I WANT TO be one, I didn't say I am one. So, duh! That means of course I'm not funny now, but the idea is that I WANT TO BE FUNNY! Geez Louise! When Freddy said he wanted to be a fireman I didn't hear anybody ask him how many fires he's put out lately. Arggh! It's so irritating. Next time I'll just say I want a be a teacher or a nurse. Something you can handle. But, no, I totally appreciate the lack of confidence in my real dream. You know why? Because it'll only make me work harder. I'm going to work so hard to be funny…Geez Louise. (shaking her head) And, guess what? I don't JUST want to be a comedian. I want to have a whole lot of kids too. (thinks about it) I think I want to have about 12. Uh huh. Twelve. But I want them all to be twins. Yeah, twins. They need to be twins because I have a lot of fun and creative names ready to use, and it will be a lot more fun if they're born in pairs. Like what? Well, like a boy and girl set of twins could be Candy and Soda! Two boys could be Tater and Tot. You see where I'm going here don't you? Hey, a set of triplets would be cool too. They could be Ketchup, Mustard, and Relish. Oh, I can't wait to grow up. I'm going to have so much fun. Grownups are so dumb to take everything so seriously. Look at all the fun they could be having if they'd just lighten up.

Robot-Proof Me

Hey, Mom! Hey, Dad! I know you said no to sleep away camp this year. I know you think it's expensive, and it's just a lot of arts and crafts, and putting on silly shows and singing and stuff. Well, I just read an article in the Wall Street Journal that says you really should be worrying about robot-proofing me. That's right, I said robot-proofing! The article said something like, well…it said that if you don't robot-proof me, something might happen, like I grow up and won't be able to do any job better than a robot could. And then you'll be stuck paying for my breakfast, lunch and dinner for the rest of my life. I'm guessing that could probably, would probably, add up to a whole lot of dinero. I mean, you know how I like to eat. But, there's a light at the end of the tunnel. If I can learn to be creative, I might just be better at it than any old robot could be. At sleep-away camp I can practice being creative by drawing and painting and acting and singing. Maybe even writing, too! Then, when I grow up, I might be able to get work and be happy and let some old robot do the boring stuff, like…I don't know, whatever it is you do at work that you're always saying you hate so much. Yeah, that stuff. So, you see, it might cost a lot of money to send me to sleep-away camp and it might look like I'm having too much fun, but in the end, it could be a very, very good thing. So, what's for lunch?

Scruffy Come Home

(calling loudly across the yard) Scruffy! Scruuuuufy! (sighs) (calling into the house) Mom, I can't find Scruffy! (sits on the ground cross-legged head in hands) He ran away. Again. What is it about me that Scruffy doesn't like? I know, I know, he's a dog. Dogs like to roam. They like to hang with other dogs. But…it seems kind of funny that he never runs away when Beatrice is home from college. Does he? See, I'm right. He only runs away when she's gone, and he is obviously extremely bored with me. Maybe I can learn to be more interesting. In a dog sort of way. It's true that Beatrice takes him for more walks. And, she likes to brush his hair in the evening before she goes to bed. She even lets him sleep in her bed. I can do more walks and I can brush his hair, but I think I'm gonna draw the line there. Dogs have fleas, you know! Oh, Scruffy. Maybe you just don't know how much I love you. You know, not everyone expresses love in the same way. Beatrice likes to say it all the time. (imitating Beatrice) "Oh, Scruffy, Wuffy, I just love you soooooo much." And then she plants a big kiss on him. Yep! A kiss. Not on his dog lips or anything, but kind of like on his forehead. (grimaces) That's another place I draw the line. Dog kisses. Yuck! I mean, I just show my love in a more, subtle way. I always remember to feed him. That's a really loving thing to do. And once I gave him part of my dinner. It was liver and onions, so that wasn't much of a sacrifice. Beatrice gives him anything she's got. She even gives up the pepperoni on her pizza. That's something I could work on, but it might take some time. Gee whiz, if Scruffy comes home, this time I'll try. I really will. I'll try to be as much like Beatrice as I possibly can. It might be painful, but…I love Scruffy so much. More than he'll ever know. Oh, Scruffy, please come…(suddenly sees Scruffy running towards her and gasps) SCRUFFY!! (slightly scolding) Where have you been?

Rhoda the Rhymer

(Rhoda is drawing when Kate enters. Rhoda looks up briefly and then quickly looks back down to her drawing.) Hey. Yup, I'm drawing. Nothing much. Just those apples. On the table over there. What? (looks at Kate) Mad? Do I seem mad? Nope. Not really. Not mad. Just (sighs) busy. (quietly draws for a moment and then stops) Want to hear a poem I wrote? Okay. Listen to this. It's called Roses are Red. (clears her throat) Roses are red, Violets are blue. I like Jeremy Legend, but he likes you. The end. (goes back to her drawing then looks up again) I'm not mad. I said I wasn't mad and I'm not. Life is what it is. Ya know? (drawing for another moment or two). Want to hear another poem? It's called Roses are Red part two. (clears throat again) Roses are Red, Cactus are green, if you go out with Jeremy Legend, when you know that I like him, you're just being mean. (looks at Kate) What do you think of that one? It is not unfair. It is totally true. Why? Because you don't even like Jeremy. You never even noticed him until I confided in you that I had a huge crush on him. And, now…just because…Oh, forget about it. (sighs and goes back to her drawing) I'm not giving you the silent treatment. I. Am. Drawing. (draws for a moment) Want to hear another poem. It's called Roses are…Okay, so fine, you can guess the title. Good for you. Do you want to hear it or not? (clears throat) Roses are Red, Blue is for Ink. Friends can be lovely, but sometimes they…are very inconsiderate.

The Monster in Me

I'm "an angel." I'm "just adorable." I'm "such a good student." I'm the "best daughter in the world." I'm "Daddy's little girl." I'm "Good Citizen of the Week." And, then sometimes... something snaps. And there I am. Tired of trying to be everything everybody wants. Worn out. Frayed. It's usually some little thing that break's this thirsty camel's back. And then the monster will come out to play. Out of the dungeons and caves where she hides when I'm saying "Please" and "Thank you" and "Amen." She'll slither up through the dusty caverns, leaving her slimy trail within, and bursting through corridors of thoughts all quiet, kind, studious and polite. She suddenly erupts like an angry grand volcano. Tearing and spewing out of my mouth, she comes unwelcomed like a cloud of toxic fumes garnished with a stream of burning lava. My eyes grow large with wonder at the things I hear her say. And everyone within her path looks on with utter disbelief. And then, within an hour or so, she's gone. Slithering back to her nasty lair. Curling up, like a child, to go to sleep. And then I'll cry and wish she'd go away for good. And sometimes I will almost get my wish as she'll be quiet for the longest time. It might be weeks. It might be months. And when the quiet lasts so long, I'll foolishly believe that all is well. But then some little thing occurs. A word is said, a deed is done, that wakes her from her fervent sleep. And I and all within my sight can only stop and wait to hear her reckless words, with dread and sorrow. And when she's done, I'll follow her routine with vain attempts to make amends to those I've hurt and trust that's gone for good. I'll try once more to wish the monster gone again. Never to return.

Movies and Meaning

I don't want to go. Of course I want to see the movie, but not if Clarisse is going. Yeah, she's my best friend and I love her to pieces, but I don't love seeing movies with her. She has…what I can I say…weird movie habits. Well, first of all she can never decide what to buy at the concession stand, and then she always ends up with the same thing: nachos and cheese, a hot dog with onions and relish – "extra ketchup and mustard please" and a very, very, very large soda. Diet, of course. Then, we have to find the perfect seat. Clarisse doesn't like to be too near the front or too near the back, too close to the middle, or too far to the left or right. You get the picture. So, anyway, then we find a seat, finally, and she gets all settled in with her nachos, dog, and drink and proceeds to want to tell me everything that happened to her at school that week. And she doesn't care if she's talking through all of the previews. The people around us are not amused, and neither am I. But Clarisse is oblivious. And that's not the worst thing about seeing movies with Clarisse. When the movie is over and we're on our way home, Clarissse likes to go over the movie with a fine-tooth comb and dissect it into a million parts. And even if the movie was the goofier than the Three Stooges, she has to believe it has some meaning that is deeply relevant to my life and hers. I just yawn and pretend to listen, look out the window and wonder how I got suckered into this outing once again. Like I said, Clarisse is the best, and I love her to death. She just gives movies a whole new meaning.

I'd Rather Be Tina Fey

Hey, wanna switch for a while? I'll dry, you wash? (Ally switches places with her sister Patty, and starts to dry the dishes) I can't believe mom's still on the phone out there. Do you think she's still talking to Grandma Norris? She never stays out on the patio this long anyway. She hates the mosquitos. (looks at the time) Oh my gosh, it's almost 2. Well, this is just weird. Every Saturday mom makes a huge brunch, and every Saturday we do the dishes while she takes her after brunch Saturday nap. It's like clockwork. So, what's with her today? I mean, I'm glad that she's not exhausted, it's just that I've got somewhere I need to be at 2:30 and I wasn't planning on telling mom about it. I wasn't going to lie to her, I was just going to… not worry her about it. It's not a big deal. I mean, it is actually kind of is a big deal. I mean, my whole future depends on it. No, I'm not in trouble. I just…Do you promise not to tell? Okay, here's the deal. I have an audition today at school for the Improv Players. Yes! Today at 2:30. I can't tell mom. She'll have a fit! And, I don't want to lie to her. If she'd just go in there and fall asleep like she usually does, I could leave a note like I do every Saturday and say I'm going for a bike ride. No, I haven't been lying every Saturday! I have been going for a bike ride every Saturday. But today, the one day when I wanted to do something different, she isn't taking her nap! (sighs). Yeah, I know I can tell her the truth, but you know mom. She won't like it. She wants me to be a scientist just like her. She wants me to be…Madame Curie! I mean, I like Science. I really do. It's just that, I don't want to be Madame Curie. My dream is to be Tina Fey! Mom

will never understand that. But I have to follow my dreams. I
know if I make the team, eventually I'll have to tell her. But
I'll cross that bridge when I come to it. Look, I have to leave in
ten minutes to make it to school by 2:30 on my bike. If I leave
now, while she's still on the phone, you could cover for me.
Would you? Oh please! You know you lie so much better than
I do. Well, it's true! Oh, thank you! You're wonderful! You are!
You are the best sister in the world. What should you tell her?
(thinks for a minute) I don't know. Just improvise!

The "Why" Baby

My little sister Christina is so cute. For everybody who meets her, it's love at first sight. I don't mind. I'm not jealous. I was cute once too ya know. I think it's only fair that everybody gets a turn. And I'm just glad she's not a cry baby. I mean, when she doesn't get her way, she's kind of mature about it, in a little kid kind of way. In fact, she's pretty much been that way ever since she was born. Not much of a crier. I, on the other hand…well for me it was a different story. Or so my parents say. So, I guess I can honestly say that I'm glad Christina isn't an awful lot like me. She's her own person and she should be. There's only one thing about her that, just lately, has been driving me crazy. She asks a lot of questions. Well, it's more like she just says "Why" a lot. I say, "Christina it's our turn to cross the street." "Why?" she asks. "Because the sign is showing us the little man that's walking." "Why is it a little man and not a little girl?" At this point I want to say something like, "You can't be serious." But, I just look at her and say the only thing I can say, "I don't know." At this point I would think she would be satisfied, but not Christina. She may not know exactly how annoying this is, but she will follow with a very sincere look in her eyes as she asks innocently, "Why don't you know?" (sighs) And then my reaction can vary. Depending on how many "Whys" I've fielded that day, I may be sweet and explain my ignorance on signage, or I may look up to the sky and say "Lord, give me strength." And that's when Christina will just look at me perplexed and ask, "Why are you praying in the middle of the street?" (sighs) I guess I shouldn't complain. A Why Baby is still better than a Cry Baby. And…please…. don't ask me why.

Are You Afraid to Listen?

I'm sorry if you think I talk too much. When things happen, I react. I form opinions. And for some crazy reason, I express myself. If that bothers you, maybe you should think about that. Why do my opinions make you so mad? Do you have problems expressing your own? Could it be that you're afraid? Afraid to listen to me because I'm a girl? Yeah, cause If I make sense, you might have to lie about what you think is right, just to prove to everyone else that you're smarter than me. Or better than me? You don't want to say you agree with the girl, do you? Fine, go ahead. Walk away. See if I care. (shouts after him) It's a free country, last time I checked. (to the audience) Funny, but if he would really listen to me, I'd be willing to listen to his side of the story too. And I might actually agree with some of his ideas. I mean, most of the time when I hear two sides to a situation, I feel strongly both ways. I mean, I can see that in some ways both sides of an issue are right to some degree. And I think you have to listen, and talk, and try to feel for the other person a little. Empathize, ya know, and try to understand. It's a mistake to walk away. At the end of the day, we're all in this together. We all want the world to be a better place. Not just for ourselves, but for everybody. Don't we?

Sisters

Okay, you can open your eyes now. Isn't it beautiful. (spinning around) It's my sister's prom dress. Of course she knows I'm trying it on. Claire trusts me. (sighs and puts on some dangly earrings – looks in the mirror) I can't wait to be in high school. Claire is so popular. I hope I can be just as popular as her. Claire said that as soon as I'm old enough she'll help me get a job after school at Handyman's Grocery Store. They just love her there. (brushing her hair) Basically all I'll have to do is tell them I'm her sister and I'm a shoo-in for a job as a cashier. Most girls start out bagging, but Claire says they'll just let me start as cashier if she tells them to. Cashiers get more money by the hour. Last weekend, for the holiday, Claire got time and a half. She's saving to get some fancy high-heeled shoes to go with this dress. See, if I were wearing this, I'd have to get it altered, but Claire is 5 feet 9 inches. Like a model. She can just put on some high-heeled shoes and this will fit her just right. I wish I would grow a little taller. Do you think I will? Why should you want to be any taller? Well, your whole family is short aren't they? I'm the only little one in our bunch. It makes me look awkward. I don't like being called Peanut. You only think it's cute because nobody calls you that. Nobody calls you anything funny cause you're so pretty. I feel sorry for you though. Cause you don't have a sister, like I do. It must get awful lonely being the only girl in a house full of boys. Well, I don't think you could possibly know what you're missing out on, so I'm not surprised that you don't feel sorry for yourself. Having a sister is just... well, something that you have to expe-

Continued

rience I guess. The closeness, the bond. We tell each other everything. Claire and I. Things we'd never tell another soul. Like the other day, Claire told me something I just couldn't believe, and I wanted to tell you, but I didn't. Because, you know, it's a sister thing.

Tea for Two

(speaking to her web cam) Hello and welcome to this week's tea party! I'm just going to pour myself a cup of tea, while you, dear friend out there, pour yourself a lovely cup of tea as well. I've got my Dolly over here in her little chair and I'll pour a tiny little cup for Dolly. La la la (sings a tune for a moment then looks back at the camera) I'm so glad you joined me for tea today. It's such a lovely way to get together to chat. With old friends. With new friends. With people friends. And with dolly friends. You know what I want to chat about today? Today I want to chat about time travel. Yes, that's right. Time travel. Do you believe in time travel? My Dolly does. My Dolly believes in time travel. What's that Dolly? Did you hear Dolly? She just asked me how I know. Well, don't be silly Dolly, I know because she told me so. You see, my dolly told me a story about a time when she traveled back in time and met her favorite author, Mark Twain. Now dolly, that's not true. Dolly! Why you just told me this story yesterday and now you're making me look like…well, a liar. Dolly, that's not nice. What's that Dolly? Oh, you want a lump of sugar for your tea? Well, my goodness, you never take sugar. (looks at the camera) What's gotten into Dolly today? (puts a lump of sugar in Dolly's tea) There you are. One lump of sugar. (shaking her head and speaking to the camera) Well, it looks like I'm just going to have to save my topic of Time Travel for another day in the future. (thinks for a moment) Or, in the past. So, until next week dear friends. (sips on tea) Toodle-loo.

Bonkers

(Yelling at Jimmy) You are not!

(to mom) But mom! But he… I'll quit yelling if he quits lying. He said that you told him that Dad said Jimmy is smarter than me.

Yeah, Jimmy, why did you say that?

You did, too! Just cause Dad's not here, he thinks he can say anything!

Now look what you did! You made mom cry! Me? I didn't do anything! I'm just trying to defend myself. You started it! I'm sorry, Mom. Please don't cry. Please. Please. Okay, we'll stop fighting. (gives Jimmy a look) Right, Jimmy? I said we'll stop fighting. Right? Right? Okay great, now he's ignoring me. That's fine. Don't talk to me. See if I care. In fact, that's just perfect. I don't want to talk to you anyway. Why would I. Mom, I'm sorry. Even if Jimmy's a baby and won't agree not to fight, I'll make sure it doesn't happen again. I'm the grown up one around here and Jimmy's a…What did you just say? Mom! Did you hear what he just called me?

Twelve Going on Thirty

(at school eating lunch) I want to be a doctor when I grow up. Yesterday, I took my sister Cammie to the doctor on the bus. She had a terrible sore throat that wouldn't go away. Do you want your tater tots? Yeah, okay. Dumb question. I'm so hungry! Yeah, so like I was saying, yesterday, I was absent because I had to take Cammie to the doctor. My mom can't just take a day off whenever she wants like your mom. I can make up my work tonight. After I make dinner and do the dishes. Cammie's sick and my mom works a double shift on Tuesdays. Yeah, I know you could never have my life. You're just a kid. You wouldn't last a day. Ha! Age means nothing. So what if we're both the same age. Age is just a number. My mom says I'm twelve going on 30. It's just my life. It's where I've been and things I've seen and responsibilities. That's what makes you who you are. Not age. My mom always says it's the way you handle life that matters. Attitude. That's why I get so mad when a grownup acts like a jerk, and everyone says, "He's acting like a child!" What an insult! Children are some of the nicest people I know. I mean, I sort of am one. Well, at least for another year. Then I'll be a teenager. Wow! Gosh, I could eat a cow!

Who Is the Real Me?

It's crazy. I just can't help myself. I am like fifty different people every day. No kidding. Okay. I mean, it's not like I'm actually crazy. It's not like I have fifty different names and sometimes I'll ask you to call me Andie and sometimes I'm Carol. No, it's just that I change based on who I'm around. It's just something I've always done. Like when I go to the library to help Mrs. Brown, I'm like this little sweet book worm, and I hear my voice talking to her and I sound like a mouse. Then, when I go to lunch and sit with Jerry and Jane, I act all girly and fashionista. Cause that's what they're like. We talk about going to the mall on the weekend and getting new clothes, and stuff like that. But after school, I'm like a tomboy. I'm all about running and basketball and playing with my brother and his friends until mom yells that it's time for dinner. I could go on and on. Sometimes it gets weird. Like one day when Jerry and Jane showed up in the library cause they had to do a book report. I hid behind a book shelf and then I told Mrs. Brown that I had a stomach ache and had to go to the clinic. I ran out of that library as fast as I could. They just wouldn't understand if they saw that side of me. My Dad says it's fine and that most people have more than one side to their personality. But, I think I'm a little extreme. You know, like the snow boarder who does like fifty flips in the air while everybody else only does three. Being so many different versions of me can sometimes make my head spin. It's like, sometimes I just wonder, who is the real me?

Once Upon a Time

Things haven't been so good lately. We moved from my country and my mother married Edward. He doesn't like me. Mom says I need to respect him and give it time. But time doesn't seem to heal all things. With each new day I seem to find another way to humiliate myself. Do something wrong. Say something infuriating. It's a talent I never knew I had. And suddenly although some people say I'm very small, I seem to take up an enormous amount of space. I'm always in the way. Out here, when I climb this tree, I feel a little free. Up here where no one can see, I can dream of my old home and remember a life that was happier for me. Where I had friends that somehow cared for me. And I could make them smile, or even laugh, or maybe be there when they needed me. Yes, I try to remember, even when it brings a tear. That once upon a time, in a land far away, I did something right.

Shy

I hate being shy. It's worse than…I don't know…all the other rotten stuff that nobody wants to be. It's how my parents introduce me to their new "friends" and "business acquaintances." "Oh, this is our other daughter, Marjorie. She's the shy one of the family." That's because my other two sisters Bridget and Bonnie are totally "gregarious" and "so much fun to be around." My grannie always says, "That Bonnie! She never met a stranger!" And my teacher Mrs. Spam "just can't believe" I'm nothing like my chatter box sister Bridge." Everyone calls her Bridge cause it's short and cute just like she is. Lately, I've been thinking about how shy I am. I looked up all sorts of self-help advice on how to re-invent myself and I even tried a few of their ideas. But it's hard. Especially because everyone thinks of me as shy and expects me to be shy. So, it feels like being anything else is virtually impossible. Sometimes I think I'd be better off moving to another country. If I could go where nobody knows me, I could start all over again and be loud, opinionated, and daring. I haven't told anyone how I feel of course. Except you. I doubt I'll ever tell anyone again. After all that is my greatest talent. Keeping all my thoughts and feelings to myself. Maybe I'll start an online club and ask other shy kids to join. I won't use my real name, I'll use a pseudonym. Something like The Quiet Girl, or Little Miss Invisible. (sighs) Those are names I've been called before. But when I think about those names, I get kind of angry. You know, mad at everyone who called me those names and mad at me for taking it. I mean being shy is not a crime. And it's not the only thing that defines me. I like to draw, I love to horseback ride. And I can beat Bridget and Bonnie in a game of scrabble any day. And when I think about it, I'm glad there are shy people like me in the world. Imagine the world without shy people. No one would ever shut up and listen. Is that the kind of world that anyone would want to live in? Gosh! There has to be someone to listen to all that chatter. (smiling) Thank goodness there are shy people like me!

Love Happens

Hey Quinn. Whatcha up to? Guess who's in love? Yeah it happened to me.

Nope. I'm not gonna tell. He's someone you know. But you'll
never guess. Not in two million years. And no, I won't tell you if
you get it right. That is too fair. I'm in love, and I'm takin' it to
my grave. Even he won't ever know. Cause that's just how I am.
But it's real. I can feel it. For the first time I feel it. I couldn't
tell him! What if he doesn't like me? Nah! He doesn't. Believe
me – he does not. But that's okay. As long as I can admire him
from afar. And dream. Well, that one day, we'll somehow be
together. Married. Well, it's just a dream! For goodness sake.
Yes, I'll invite you! You'd be my, you know, Maid of Honor. But
I get to wear the pretty white dress. Yours will be all poofy and
pink. Yeah, one day. Unless. Well, you know. I change my mind.
And fall in love with someone else. I mean, if this could happen
to me today, the first day of fifth grade, who knows what could
happen to me tomorrow. I guess it's how things are, now that
I'm not a little kid anymore. You know, love happens.

Things I Can't Say

I don't like her. She makes me feel…weird. Like I'm weird.
Always asking me questions about how I feel. I don't feel
anything. I'm trying not to feel anything. I'm trying to forget
about everything for a while and just get by. Without being
noticed. Why does she notice me so much? Why does she care?
She doesn't really care. She's just doing her job. Turning in
some report about the weird kid who never talks to anyone.
The kid who looks sad and troubled. And that kid just happens to be me. She doesn't care about me at all. So why should
I talk to her? Why should she be the one that I suddenly open
up to and share everything with? What's so special about her?
Why doesn't she just ask me the same question everybody else
eventually asks? "Why are you so quiet?" And then I can give
them my standard response. My biggest, fattest lie. "I just don't
have anything to say." And they usually accept that. I'm boring. I'm stupid. I'm the least interesting, most apathetic person
in the world. But the truth is I'm nothing but boring. If I told
them my real story, they'd find it very, very interesting. But that
wouldn't make them like me. They'd want nothing to do with
me, just like things are now. Because nobody wants to hear
what I would tell them. There are things you just don't say.

Hello Tree

Hello tree. I've got some sad news. We're moving today.
What am I going to do without you? We've lived here
together since I was born. But I don't remember you then.
I just remember the first time we talked. I was five years
old. Do you remember? Tammy and Lindsay were going
to camp and I was too little to go. I cried and ran out here
when it was time for everyone to see them off. I stood behind
you so that no one could see me. And I imagined that you
asked me just exactly what was wrong. I even imagined your
lovely kind voice. It was like, "Hello, Little Raindrop, why
are your crying?" I know you probably sound much lovelier
than that. Like the way you sound when the wind rustles
through your leaves. (sighs) And then I told you about how
sad I felt that I was the youngest one and always being left
out of things. You listened. And I knew that you understood.
And you cared. And ever since then, you've been my best,
and sometimes my only, friend. Oh, what will I do without
you tree? Will I ever see you again? We're moving thousands
and thousands of miles away to a place where I don't even
think trees grow. Even though they call it the Big Apple. I
think it's all sidewalks and skyscrapers and smog. I wish I
could write to you, and let you know. Dear tree! How can I
say the only thing we've never, ever, said before? (closes her
eyes for a moment, then looks at the tree) Goodbye.

Anyone but Me

It's going great. Like I said, everyone thinks I'm fabulous. The problem is, everyone thinks I'm fabulous at improv. No one thinks I'm fabulous personally. No one even says a word to me in class until we're in a scene together. I guess I don't say a word to them either. I'm shy. I never know what to say. In a scene, that's different. Then I'm not myself. I'm somebody else. I'm a little girl throwing a tantrum, or an old lady waiting for a bus. I can talk with a funny voice or use a southern accent. It's not a very good southern accent, but it's a funny one. And everyone in the class is in stitches. They say I make the funniest faces too. The teacher, Miss Fallas, always asks the class to discuss what worked about the scene. She says, (imitating Miss Fallas) "That was beautiful. Anyone want to share your thoughts?" And the kids all say amazing and wonderful things about me. Cause I'm somebody else when I'm on that stage. The minute I step off, I'm invisible. That's why I love improv. I can be anyone. Anyone at all. Anyone but me!

Literal Lottie

She's my best friend, but sometimes she just doesn't get me.
Like, if I say something's happened to me and it's the "end of
the world," she really thinks I mean it's the end of the world.
You know, sometimes she just doesn't get it when I exaggerate.
Like, if I said I was "in a jam," she probably would think that
I'm literally in a jar. (laughs) So, anyway, that's why I call her
Literal Lottie. Sometimes, of course, I call her other things.
Nice things. Like, sometimes, when she is so adorable and sweet
and bakes my favorite cookies, because she knows I had a really
bad day. Then, I call her Loveable Lottie. Or, when I'm telling
jokes, and she's laughing so hard that she's telling me to stop,
cause if I say one more funny thing, her sides will split open.
Then, I call her Laugh-a-lot Lottie. Then there's Liverwurst
Lottie. There's a long story I could tell you about that one, but
I think you probably just had to be there. And Lolligag Lottie,
which is why she has more tardies than anyone in our class.
And then there's Little-Lyin Lottie. Oops. That may be the
only one that's not so nice. But she knows why I call her that.
She'd kill me if I told you. But, I say it with the greatest affec-
tion. I really do. I guess my point is that I pretty much never
call her just Lottie. That just wouldn't be right. I mean, she's a
lottie more than just Lottie. Haha. A lottie more than Lottie.
That one would have her rolling on the floor.

There's a Monster in My Macaroni

Help! Ms. Adelaide! There's a monster in my macaroni! (runs to stage right and mimes grabbing the arm of Adelaide and pulling her over) See it's… (looks in her plate and then around the room) Where did it go? It was right here. It started out looking just like a noodle and then it came up out of the cheese and turned red and blue and green and it growled and Ms. Adelaide!! Stop laughing at me! This is serious. This is colossal. (still looking around the room) This is…typical. Believe me, I am not crazy. I am not a troublemaker. It's the monster. Apparently, I'm dealing with a monster with a very warped sense of humor. A monster who likes to play jokes. Especially on me. Never mind, Ms. Adelaide, go back to whatever important thing it was you were doing before I interrupted you. I promise that I won't bother you any more with any of my trivial, nonsensical monster sightings. You're probably right. I'm bonkers. Please, just go right on ignoring me. (under her breath) You usually do anyway. What? Oh, I didn't say anything. No, no, you're doing just fine over there watching tv or texting your bingo club, or whatever it is you're doing while you're not watching me. No, no, no, you're an absolutely fabulous sitter. My parents would be thrilled. And besides, I've been telling my parents for years that I don't need a sitter. I'm almost thirteen and I can deal with my monster-filled macaroni on my own. Dealing with monsters is probably not in your job description anyway. No worries, Ms. Adelaide. I'll call you when I need you. (talking to herself) I'll just finish this delicious microwave macaroni that Ms. Adelaide made for me. Mmm. Yumm! It is

Continued

just delicious. And I am not being sarcastic. Heck, kids my age don't even know what sarcastic means. (sarcastically) This so yummy (taking a big bite). Sadly, I'll just take a few more bites and it will all be gone. (taking another huge bite) Down the hatch. (swallowing hard) Down the.... (gulping and screeching) Ms. Adelaide!!!! I just swallowed the monster!!!!

The Not-Nicest Camper of Them All

At the end of the summer, I got picked as the Nicest Camper and I felt so guilty. Is there a superlative prize for the not-nicest camper? The most judgmental camper? Well, if you're wondering why, I'll explain. You see, when I first got to camp, I walked into my cabin and I just knew I was doomed. I thought Candy was too chubby and would totally screw up our rowing team. I thought Carly looked too nerdy, like she'd never be able to hold her own in the Crazy Danceathon. In fact, I had the wrong idea about every single girl. I just knew I'd be bored all summer, and they just couldn't measure up to fun, cool, charismatic me. Boy was I wrong. As the days passed, I learned that Candy cannot only row, she can also be hilariously funny. And Carly is not only really smart, but she can also dance like the craziest kid in town. And me? As it turns out, I'm not always as fun, cool and charismatic as I think I am. But, in spite of my shortcomings, my new friends were good friends to me. When I didn't do so well at rowing or dancing, they were there for me. They cared about me. They made the summer go by like a breeze. And then they surprised me by nominating me for the Nicest Camper. I felt so guilty. And then I won, and that was even worse! But then, I thought about it. I may not have started out as the nicest camper, but I did learn that I can be wrong. And, I learned that not only can you not judge a book by its cover, but you can't judge people by your first, sometimes wrong, impression. Preconceived notions and assumptions can be dead wrong. I guess I learned a lot this summer, and I grew. And not just a half an inch in height, but an inch in my head,

Continued

too. Or was it my heart? Anyway, I became a bigger person this
summer. And that, makes me feel really nice.

There's a Sailboat in my Soup

My dad gets so mad because I eat too slow. Well, I play with my food. I'm dreamy. He thinks I do it on purpose, just to make him mad. I don't. And Callie is always kicking me under the table. She hates it when dad gets mad. Even if it has nothing to do with her. She says it will make his blood pressure go up and it puts her stomach in a ginormous knot and makes her break out. You know, zits all over her face. That's a very big deal to her right now because she's trying to get our new neighbor Tommy Brazenlifter to ask her out on a date. Personally, I don't think Tommy knows she's alive, zits or no zits. And, in any case, I can't be held responsible for her love life or dad's blood pressure for that matter. I really, really, really don't eat slow or play with my food on purpose. I don't want to make anyone mad. Scout's honor. It's just…well, I start eating and thinking, and Callie usually starts rambling. You know, going on and on about her day at school. How great she was at the softball game. Or, whatever cute guy smiled at her. Whatever snobby girl made her mad. I suddenly find myself tuning her out. I look at the broccoli on my plate and I start to see something different. I mean, instead of plain boring old broccoli, I see a forest in Madagascar. I take a wad of butter and put it on my broccoli and suddenly it becomes a lemur jumping from one stalk of broccoli to the next. And, then there's my cooked carrots which sometimes look like alien saucers. Dad gets furious. Sometimes he's been yelling at me for about five minutes before I even notice. My shins are bruised from Callie's kicks, and I look up with a grin. Last night, I made them both so mad I think steam

Continued

came out of their ears. Dad looked at me and said how can you just sit there and fiddle-faddle? Why don't you eat? I just grinned and pointed to my minestrone. "There's a sailboat in my soup." Callie and Dad just couldn't see it, which is too bad for them. I mean, I think they're really missing out, don't you?

Dear Mable Massiwash-Macabee

My pen pal is awesome. She has the answer to everything!!
Seriously. And I can tell her anything. Anything at all. Seriously.
But, sometimes it is soooo hard waiting to hear back from her.
I mean, we decided from the get-go that we would do snail
mail. You know, do things the old-fashioned way. Well, that was
kind of Mrs. Sharktank's idea. It means we can't just whip off a
response without giving it a lot of thought. Mrs. Sharktank says
we should sometimes think about what we say before we say it.
And learn to use better words than we already know. Like get a
better vocabulary. Mrs. Sharktank. She was an awesome fifth-
grade teacher. The pen pal thing was her idea. She was just the
best. I really miss Mrs. Sharktank. Seriously. She arranged the
whole pen pal thing with her teacher friends across the world.
Mrs. Sharktank gets around. She travels every summer during vacation and visits all sorts of interesting places. She's even
been to Paris. That's my dream vacation. Paris. (sighs) But my
pen pal doesn't live in Paris. She just lives in plain old Bakers-
field. That's in California. But she is soooo smart. She reads a
lot. But more than that, she's really wise. And not wise like in
wisenheimer. You know, wisenheimer, like a smarty pants sort
of thing. My grandma Josephine likes to call me that when I get
snotty. No, my pen pal isn't a wisenheimer. She's just wise. Like
an owl, I guess. And she's different, too. I mean, she's not like
other kids I know. For one thing, she always addresses me with
my first and last name and she signs with her full name too.
She's very grown up that way. At first, I thought that was weird,
but then I realized that she's just different and different is good.

Continued

Different as it turns out is not the same as weird at all. I mean, I can ask her anything and she gives me tons of great advice. She writes super long and super interesting letters. Mine are actually kind of short, but she says she doesn't mind. She's soooo great. (sits down at desk and pulls out paper and pen to write) Today, I need to write to find out if I should tell Alexander Ritchie that I'm his secret admirer. She'll know exactly what to do. (writing) Dear Mable Massiwash-Macabee, I need your advice regarding a very serious (thinks for a moment) dilemma... (smiles, then to the audience) Mabel uses that word all the time. Seriously.

You'll Never Guess

Be careful what you wish for. My mother always says that to me. I like to make wishes and then spend the day dreaming they'll come true. Last year I was so bored on my birthday that I made a wish that my next birthday would be the most magical ever. Then a whole year went by and I almost forgot. Until... the day before my birthday, my thirteenth birthday, a package arrived in the mail. My mom hadn't gotten home from work yet, so I was the only one in the house. I tore open the package. Inside there was a letter, a chocolate brownie, and a deck of cards sealed tight. The letter said, "Dear Wish Monger, I know that you are always making wishes, but last year on your birthday you made a wish that is about to come true. Tomorrow, your birthday, is going to be the most magical ever. Tonight, at five minutes before midnight, go to your most secret place. There you will eat the brownie and then open the deck of cards. Say this rhyme and turn over the card on top and you'll reveal a number. Whatever number pops up, that will be the age you'll be on your birthday tomorrow and for the rest of the year. If you don't do this, you'll revert back to age one and start your life all over again." I couldn't believe my eyes. Revert back to one? Oh no! And what if I turned the card over and I suddenly turned 98. I was really, really looking forward to being 13. I couldn't eat dinner that night I was so nervous. Mom asked if anything was wrong and I squeaked out a "no." I went to bed early but had no plans to go to sleep. I just kept wishing, please, please, please, just let me be thirteen tomorrow. I don't care if it's magical at all. I watched the clock and just before

Continued

midnight I snuck up to the attic with the brownie, the letter and the cards. At five minutes till, I ate the brownie – it was really good - and then I said the rhyme. "One, Two, Fifteen, Three – just how old will I be?" My hands were trembling, but I slowly turned over the top card. You know what it said? You'll never guess. It said, "Happy Thirteenth birthday! Lucky you – you get to be thirteen for the whole next year. Isn't that magical? Love, Mom!"

My Short Story Came to Life

Mr. Addleson, do you have a minute? I have a problem. Well, no, it's not personal. No, I don't need to see the guidance counselor! It's about…my short story. No, Mr. Addleson, I'm not here to complain about my grade. A B- wasn't what I wanted, but I was totally okay with it. I mean, that's the first short story I've ever written. Well, yes, I know that's the fifth one we've turned in, but my mother kind of wrote most of the other ones. I know, I know, that's terrible. It is. She just wanted to help. And, I'm totally sorry I let her. That's why I wrote this one myself. And yes, I know that just because I confessed it doesn't mean I won't be punished, but Mr. Addleson, I have a much bigger problem than that. My short story came to life! Yes, I know, I know, I know that even though you gave it a B- minus you told me, you said that I should keep on trying because it was "vivid and colorful," and I totally appreciate that. But, that's not what I'm talking about. Mr. Addleson, my story, my characters were so vivid and colorful that they…CAME TO LIFE! Not just on the page, but here. AT SCHOOL. Yes, Mr. Addleson, they are walking around Grossmont Middle today. I just bumped into Alisson Able, and her mother too! Yes, yes, that's right, the snotty cheerleader with a little bit of a lisp. Yes, and her mother with the giant mole on the end of her chin. Oh, my gosh, Mr. Addleson, I just about jumped out of my skin. I said, "What are you doing here?" Jane just rolled her eyes and said, "Who are you and why are talking to me?" But her mother gave Jane's ponytail a yank and said "Don't be rude, Jane! Young lady, we're here to see the principal. Where

Continued

in the world is his office? Jane seems to have forgotten the way, but then again, she'd forget her own head if it wasn't connected to her body." It was so strange. I think my jaw was probably on the floor, but I pointed in the direction of Mr. Peter's office and Mrs. Able took Jane by the arm and drug her away. It was so strange. I mean, I don't even like Jane. I didn't like her from the moment I made her up. But, seeing her mother yank on her ponytail and drag her by the elbow made me feel sorry for her. It was so strange. And then I realized, oh my gosh! They aren't even real. What are they doing here? Mr. Addleson, you have to help!

Tchaikovsky and Me

And, that's why I find it hard to make friends. But I loved living with Grandma and Grandpa. And if I could go back and have things turn out differently, I really don't think I would. I mean, let's say for example my mother had asked me to go to Paris with her, instead of leaving me at the farm. (sighs) It doesn't really matter anyway, does it? She didn't ask me to go and Grandpa and Grandma and I had a wonderful life. But it's weird now being with kids who have crushes on celebrities that I've never even heard of and I've got a crush on Cary Grant. Oh yeah, we used to watch old movies all the time. Just about every night. Grandma would get all cozy with her blanket wrapped around her shoulders and grandpa would make the popcorn. Not in the microwave. In an iron skillet. I think it was kind of cool, but other kids just don't get it. But then there's Tchaikovsky. He seems to understand me. He's different, too. He loves music. Not modern music, but classical musical. That's why I gave him that nickname, Tchaikovsky. His real name is Aaron. He's just not a regular kid. You know what he said the other day? He said, "I'm so glad I didn't live before Gershwin. I just couldn't imagine never getting to hear Rhapsody in Blue." Gosh! He's the first real friend I've ever had.

The Beginning, Middle, and the End

It was a stormy relationship. It was! I'm not exaggerating! I do not always exaggerate! Let me tell you the story. No, I haven't. I have not told you the whole story. I told you pretty much how it ended. That Harper and I are no longer friends. We're used-to-be's. Or, UTBBFFs. But, and that's a BIG But – ha ha, as you are probably aware, every story has a beginning, middle and an end. So, you're missing two of the parts. So, you really don't have a clue about Harper and me. You, like, have the tip of the iceberg. Or, let's say one grain of sand on a whole big sandy beach. Or, one flea on a big hairy dog named Bo. Okay, okay. I know you get what I mean, so can I tell you the story now? Puh- leeze!!! Puh-leeze!!! Oh, come on. Pretty please with a cherry on top? Cause I want to tell somebody. Puh-leeze!! I have to tell somebody. Not just anybody. I want to tell you!. Cause you are my new BFF. My better BFF. My best BFF. My amazingly fabulous better new best BFF. That's MAFBNBBFF! That's pretty awesome right? So, come on MAFBNBFF, let me spill my guts to you so we won't become UTBBFFs. Used-to-be's. No, it's not an ultimatum. And, yes, I do know what that means. Geez. Now you're sounding like a wise guy. A smarty pants. Sounding a little bit like Harper used to sound, in the beginning...

Something is Wrong With Me

Something is wrong. With me. Every day I find myself in
these situations where…all the pieces come together. All the
right players are in the room. Like, everything is set just right.
I mean, like if someone were writing a play it would be like,
"cute guy walks into room where girl with a huge crush on him
sits reading a book." And in the play, she says something funny
or cute and he laughs, and they fall madly in love and walk
through the halls for the rest of the year, hand in hand. But in
my world, it's cute guy walks into the room and girl with huge
crush on him turns to ice. Frozen. Unable to speak or to move.
He asks her what she's up to and she says something stupid like,
"What?" Or, "What does it look like I'm doing? I'm reading a
book!" I don't know how to be funny, or cute, when the time is
right. Sure, I can be hilarious and adorable at home with Dad,
at the dining room table, but that's not doing me a whole heck
of a lot of good. At school, I'm like the only girl who never
goes with anyone, never gets asked to a dance, never sits with
anyone at lunch. Well, I do sit with Mable, and I know it's not
nice, but she's just like not really anyone. Like me. I mean,
we're kind of both nobodies. Oh, my goodness. (sighs) What's
the matter with me?

The Worst Part

Hmm. That's a really hard question. And, at the same time it's a really easy question. No. No, I don't dislike the question. It's a good question. You do, I mean, I think you ask…some very… some really good questions. Like this one. Hmm. Let me see. What is the worst part of having a new stepmother? Right? That was the question, wasn't it? Okay. Let me see. No, I want to answer. I do. Let's see. I can think of a lot of things, but I'm not sure which one is the worst. Yeah, really. I can think of… at least ten things. Yeah, about ten things that I don't like about having a new stepmother. Should I go ahead and make a list? Sort of a top ten things that are the worst part of having a new stepmother? Okay. This will be fun. This might be the most fun I've had all day. Heck, it might be the most fun I've had all week. Okay, okay, I'll get started.

Number ten. The tenth worst part about having a new step-mother is that I have to clean my room. My mother never really made me clean my room. She sort of insinuated that it would be nice if I'd clean my room, but she didn't come in and judge me or belittle me, or threaten to take my stuff if I didn't put it away. Okay, nine. The ninth worst thing is that I have to go to camp so that my dad and you-know-who can have a romantic summer together, sort of like a second honeymoon. Eight - I have to take out the garbage. Every day! Seven - I don't get to talk to my dad when he comes in the door from work. She's got first dibs, and I don't even want to be around for all the lovey-dovey. Six - I have to be in bed every night at nine, and I have to show her my homework when it's finished. Five – She is a teacher at my school and all the kids hate her. Which means they all either feel sorry for me or hate me too.

Four – She thinks I'm too old for comic books. Three – She thinks I'm too old for cartoons.

Two – My dad thinks she's an angel and can do no wrong. In any situation, he'll take her side.

And one. Well, that's the easy part. She had this big idea that I should come talk to you. Her shrink. And, of course, I know that you'll tell her everything I say, and she'll just love that. Did you get all that by the way? I hope you don't leave anything out.

The Perfect Boy

Jeffrey Boyd is not the perfect boy! You are just crazy in love. That's why they say, "love is blind," silly. Don't be mad at me. I just don't have a crush on him like you do. I don't have a crush on anybody. I wish we'd get a new boy in school. A new boy who would really, really be perfect. Oh Geez-Louise, Barron Sharp is not perfect. Are you kidding? He does have nice eyes. Yeah. He probably has the most beautiful eyes in the whole school. And your Jeffrey has nice teeth. A nice smile. He is too your Jeffrey. Well, he probably would be yours if you would just tell him how much you like him. How you adore him! How you think he's the most perfect boy in the entire universe. Ha! You're blushing. You are! You're turning red like a beet. (laughs) You are too. No, the perfect boy doesn't exist for me, but if I could put about five different boys in a blender and mix them up, I could probably get close to making a perfect boy. It would be so cool if I could just make the perfect boy recipe. You know, Jeffrey's smile, Barron's eyes, Chad Little's sense of humor. You don't think he's funny? Are you crazy? He always makes me laugh so hard. And then there's Linus Frisby's name. I mean, how awesome would that be to go with a guy named Linus Frisby. If only he weren't such a nerd. Maybe when he gets older, he won't be such a nerd and we can get married. It would be so awesome to be Mrs. Frisby.

Mother Knows Best?

I am so not like you. Why do we get along? Did you know you're the first boyfriend I've ever had? Oh, yeah, I did say that before about a million times, didn't I? But that's what you love about me right? That I repeat myself over and over and over again, but it's always about you. That's one thing my mom taught me about boys. Well, she said "men" technically, but I think it applies to boys, too. Oh, just that men never get tired of hearing about themselves. Or, maybe she said, "talking about themselves." Anyway, in either case I think it's true. Don't you? Are you listening? Oh, hey that's a really cool shirt you're wearing. Tell me again about the way you love cars. I just never get tired of hearing it. And after that tell me about how you like to put apple sauce on your pancakes, and how, when you were little, you used to eat lingonberries that your mom had flown all the way in from Sweden. Go ahead. I'm all ears. Gosh, I just love lingonberries!

WYSIWYG

That's a picture of me, my brother, and our mom and dad. We look nice, and we are nice. Really. My mom calls us a WYSIWYG (pronounced "wiz-ee-wig") family. What You See Is What You Get. She didn't make up that saying, but she's probably the first person who used it to describe us. Maybe. But, anyway, I think she's right. In fact, we are so WYSIWYG that I think we're kind of boring. I mean, with us, there's not a lot of mystery or surprises. Not like with Jennifer's family. Last week I went over to spend the night with Jennifer for her birthday. It was supposed to be a slumber party, but for some strange reason everyone called at the last minute and couldn't come. I had never met anyone in Jennifer's family, but I'd seen a picture in the school directory. We have this cool section where every kid can post a picture of them and their parents and brothers and sisters and pets or whatever they want. Jimmy Long posted a picture of him and his Grammie and Auntie, cause that's who he lives with. They look kind of scary-mean, so I hope they're not WYSIWYG, but anyway I digress. Jennifer's family looked really average, and nice and I wasn't too concerned about staying with them for one night and all. But, it wasn't long after I arrived that I knew, they were definitely on their best behavior in that shot. First of all, her mom was raging mad because the other girls had all ditched. And then her dad found her mom's ranting just hilarious and couldn't stop laughing. Her brother wouldn't talk to anyone at all, and Jennifer said that he is totally on strike and hasn't said a word since, like the day after his seventh birthday, when he didn't get the video game that he wanted. And then, to top it all off, I accidentally sat down in the dog's spot on the sofa, and he ran right over and bit me on the leg. It was just a small bite, but it bled! And it hurt like mad. Yeah, that little chihuahua Peppy and I definitely did not make friends. I ended up having to call my mom and go home, after we went to Urgent Care. I felt sad that the night hadn't worked out. I thought it was going to be so much fun. I felt sorry for Jennifer too. I looked at the school directory when I got home to show my mom the picture of Peppy. He looked so sweet and I swear he was even smiling. What you see is definitely not always what you get.

Stuck with That

Stuck with That. I wrote that poem about something that she said to me. In front of everyone. She thought she could humiliate me into being who she wanted me to be. Shame on me for not being everything that she is, and more. Just make fun of my weakness and it will go away. And she felt so good about herself because it did seem to go away. Because I was afraid. Afraid to let her know that deep inside I am still "a coward." The fear is always there. Imagine that. The daughter of someone everyone reveres. Some would say the best performer in the world. Yeah, I started to pretend that everything was fine. And sometimes, I believe the lie myself. And I hear her making fun of others and secretly I cringe. If she only knew that I am still "the idiot." The fool that she so hates for me to be. I am not the image of her likeness. I have weaknesses that other people have, and I wish that I could tell her that. But she wouldn't hear of it. It would make her very angry, and oh so sad, and then she would attack me with her words and I'd feel small. Then I would be crushed. So, I keep pretending that I'm not the girl I am, and everyone thinks I'm fine. But I always remember the words she used to shame me, and I know that deep inside, no matter where I go, I'm stuck with that.

Your Armpits May Be Crazy, but My Big Toe is Psycho

Okay, okay, I know. You've always got bigger problems than me. Like your armpits are crazy, right? You don't remember telling me about that? How they talk to you and all that stuff. Of course, they'd never talk to you in front of me, right? Oh, so now you remember? It's all coming back to you now? Well, I've got news for you. You are not the only one with weird problems. Your armpits may be crazy, but my big toe is psycho. Yeah, P.S.Y.C.H.O. Psycho! I figured it out the other night. I was lying in bed and my mom poked her head in the door like she always does and said you better start sleeping because you've got a test tomorrow morning at 7:45 AM! And this voice that sounds like me goes, "What does it look like I'm trying to do?!." And boy did my mom get mad! And, that wasn't the first time that's happened. So, yeah, anyway, I figured it out. Cause this time I could hear exactly where it was coming from. It was my doggone big toe talking! It was! I swear it! I know it sounds crazy. My mom didn't believe it either. She just shook her head and said "Mmm, mmm, mmm. You need to show me a little respect." But, girl, I'm telling you my big toe is just psycho! I don't even know how you can be laughing at me. You're one to talk, with your stupid crazy armpits and all that. And, no, I cannot make my big toe talk in front of you! I don't know if it's shy or if it just doesn't like you, but girl, if you think my big toe will talk in front of you, you're as crazy as your arm pits.

My Happy Ending

My dad is a famous writer, but I don't tell other kids that. I'm only telling you because I'm just about 130 percent sure that I'll never see you again in my life. And…even though I told you that my dad is famous, I'm not going to tell you who he is. I will give you one little hint though. My dad writes kids' books. That is, books for kids. Kids about my age. And your age. In fact, he gets a lot of his ideas – he says – by eavesdropping on me and my friends when we hang out. Of course, they all think he's a dentist. That's what I told them. And he writes using a pseudonym. You know, a fake name. So, they don't suspect a thing. Tommy Tuttle is the only kid who ever seemed a bit suspicious. He got invited to my birthday party last year, and when he saw the size of our heated swimming pool with its super awesome slide, and hot tub shaped like a famous mouse, he said, "Boy, your dad sure must fill a lot of cavities!" I said, "Oh yeah, he does. He pulls a lot of teeth, too! Mostly famous ones." That should be totally believable. We do live in Beverly Hills. I know, it sounds like I'm bragging. I guess, I am sort of. Why not? Anyone who has a reason to brag ought to have the right to do a little bragging, once in a while. My mother says I like tooting my own horn. My dad just laughs. My mom and dad are the greatest though. They always both give me the best advice. The problem is…I don't always follow it. I guess I like to have a mind of my own. Like when I write stories. Dad reads them and gives me his honest critique. Usually, he likes my stories until the ending. Dad says that kids have to have a happy ending. I don't see it that way. I mean, I just want to know what happens in the end. The whole truth and nothing but the truth. And my characters usually have friendships that end and get bad grades on tests they studied for all year. You know, they're real tear jerkers. Dad just can't handle all that. I write my stories my way no matter what dad says. And, you know what? That's my happy ending!

33 Things

My mom won't let me whine to her the way you do with your mom. I mean, I used to sound just like you. (with whiny voice) "I hate my hair." "I hate Mrs. Riddensteiner's class!" "I don't want to go to aftercare!" I used to drive my mom crazy. But then she laid down the law and came up with 33 Things. When she first told me, I thought I would go insane. She said I wasn't allowed to complain or whine to her until I told her 33 things I was grateful for or happy about. If I even opened my mouth with a negative thought, she stopped me in my tracks. (in a mother's stern voice) "Uh,uh, remember, 33 Things Briana, please!" So, when she wanted me to wear this stupid sweater that my Aunt Augusta gave me last Christmas, I wanted to scream. But then I went in my room and made a list and did some rehearsing. Now, I can go through my 33 things so fast it will make your head spin. It goes something like this. "Mom, I'm grateful for (really fast) spaghetti and meatballs, bacon and peas, that pretty red skirt that goes down to my knees, bubbles and ice-cream, and underwear too, parties, and pebbles that don't get stuck in my shoe, t.v. and movies, gram and granddad, licorice, and pizza, and surfing with dad, Stevie and Bobby and all of the cats, dancing and singing and Halloween bats, sleepovers, birthdays, skiing and snow, cookies, and cupcakes, and things that I know, Saturdays, Sundays, the last day of school, but I can't stand this sweater cause it's really not cool!

All I Want for Christmas

Last year I wanted so many things. I had a list that I kept track of all year. And I got most of the stuff on my list, too. So, that was really cool. I remember thinking that was absolutely the best Christmas ever. But now, I look back on that year and that Christmas and I feel like I've grown up so much since then. So many things have happened. It's like I went from twelve to twenty. I know now that the universe doesn't rotate around me and the things that I want. There are so many people out there with nothing. Literally nothing. And so many people without a family to love. In a way I wish I was still that naïve little girl who thought that all I needed to be happy was a long list of things. But, actually, I'm glad to have become the girl that I am now. I don't want a bunch of stuff anymore. I really don't. I don't need the coolest outfit or the latest game. I want kindness and compassion, love and understanding. For everyone. For literally everyone in the world. And, I miss my family so much. I just want to go home. I want to be with the people I love and know that we are all safe and well and can hug each other and wish each other the best Christmas ever. That's all I want for Christmas now.

Hooked on Writing

It all started with Mrs. Simmons' First Annual Ten-Minute Play contest. It was a chance for me, quite possibly the only introvert in the entire Drama Club, to show what I was made of. To finally express myself. No, I did not want to audition for the spring play. And, no. I did not wish to be cast in the annual Nativity pageant. I just wanted to write a play. I just wanted to get my thoughts on paper, and then on stage, and hear my words coming out of other people's mouths. Not just anyone's mouths, mind you, but the mouths of the giants in my little world. The illustrious students. I wanted my words to come out of the mouths of the very talented and ambitious Drama Students, at Peabody Pierson Middle School – nestled somewhere between the walnuts growing in Walnut Grove, California and the peas thriving on the ridge of Pea Ridge, Tennessee. I'd like to remain slightly anonymous here, so some of the names will be changed to protect the innocent. The true location will never be revealed. A kid has to worry about things like that today, right? I mean, cyber security is great, but it all starts with tightening up the lip in my humble opinion. You know? Lock it up and throw away the key (mimes locking her lips and tossing the key). Anyway, like I said, it all started with the ten-minute play contest. I wrote a play, and everyone loved it! It was cool watching all of the kids say my lines – the words that I wrote. It was even more fun watching the audience laugh! It was extremely cool knowing they thought what I made up was funny. And that's how I got hooked. And it made me a little more popular at school, too. Now, I may be the introvert who doesn't say a word, but everyone knows I've got something pretty interesting going on in this head of mine after all.

A Valentine from March

My great-great grandmother grew up in the woods in Alleghany Valley, Pennsylvania. She was one of 6 kids and her mother and father didn't have a lot of money. Her daddy worked in the coal mines and her momma stayed at home and raised the kids. My great-grandma used to go to school in her bare feet because they couldn't afford shoes. Kids made fun of her, but she was brave. She had courage, and she went to school anyway. Her teacher loved her and knew how smart she was and wanted her to get an education. I think that makes a big difference, don't you? If you know you have somebody on your side who really cares. One year, it was Valentine's day, and my great-grandma was used to not getting any valentines at all. But, this one year, she got a really big beautiful Valentine from a super nice little girl, named March. My great-grandmother felt so proud that someone wanted to be her friend and cared. She used to talk about that "beautiful Valentine" and tell her kids and great-grandkids that it's important to notice people who could use a lift and do something nice for them. You never know how much one small act of kindness can mean to someone.

I'm Not Impressed

You're so mean. Everyone's afraid of you, and you love that, right? Well, I know you don't care, but to be totally honest with you – I'm not impressed. Being mean comes easy to you. It comes so easy to you that you probably stay up all night thinking of really rotten things you can do or say the next day. So, what! You know what would really impress me? If you would try doing something really hard for you, like being nice. Like being compassionate. Like putting somebody else's interest or needs before your own for once. I'm not sure you're capable of that. Are you? I think it might just break your brain in two if you even tried to have a nice thought. And you're not looking to do any real hard work are you? You don't even want to put in any effort at all. Because you're weak. You are the weakest person I know. It doesn't take strength to be mean. It takes strength and courage to be nice. You might want to try it sometime.

Just Friends

No, seriously, Jimmy and I are just friends. Our families have known each other forever! Since we were born. Probably before we were born! We even used to live on the same street. Carson Drive. Then, when I was five, we moved to Kensington Place. Which is still only five minutes away from Jimmy's house. So, we're like always bike riding together and sometimes their family comes over for a barbeque on the weekends. So, we are just friends. But…since you ask…I have a confession to make. I haven't told this to anyone, so you have to swear to never, ever tell a soul. Do you swear? I think I have a crush on Jimmy. Okay, I know I have a crush on Jimmy. I have a crush on him and I just can't get up the nerve to tell him. What if he doesn't like me back? I mean, I know he likes me, but does he really like me? You know what I mean?! Oh my gosh, it is driving me crazy! If he just likes me as a friend, then, if I tell him… that could end our friendship. Cause he'll feel weird around me, like I'm always thinking about how I want to hold his hand, or kiss him, or something. That could really gross him out. Oh my gosh! What should I do? I mean, sometimes it really seems like he really likes me too. Like the other day at the Halloween dance. Yeah, when he asked me to dance! I almost died. But, then right after that he asked Gretchen to dance. I think he just likes me as a friend. I do. Which is really depressing. But I'd rather be just friends than not friends at all. Wouldn't you?

The Last Day of School

I know I should be happy. It's the last day of school, for goodness sake. I mean, I've been waiting for this day all year! But, now that it's here, I'm kind of sad. I mean, of course I won't miss all the homework and I'm super glad that I get to go visit my Aunt Mazie and Cousin Lizzie in Oregon this summer, but I will miss everyone at school so much! All the kids in my class were awesome this year. I didn't think so at the start of the year, but it turned out that I made so many friends. And they're all so different. So special. We've been through a whole year of stuff together that I'll never forget. Like our field trip to the museum and Missy's amazing birthday party at the ice rink, where Logan Frost ate about 4,598 brownies. And then, there's Mrs. Groundburger. Mrs. Groundburger is, like, probably the best teacher I ever, ever had or will have. In fact, I will probably never, ever, have a teacher for the rest of my life that will even get close to the awesomeness of Mrs. Groundburger. And, it's so funny because I totally didn't like her on the first day of school and I thought it was going to be such an awful year. And, I feel so bad that I even made fun of her behind her back at lunch and called her Mrs. Hamburger. And, oh my gosh, she turned out to be (sighs) well, Mrs. Groundburger's just the best! You know what? I think I'm going to cry. It's all over. Like, the whole thing, this whole year, is just over and it is never, ever, going to happen again. I just can't believe it's the end!

About the Author

Mary Depner taught drama classes for ten years. She has performed professionally, directed countless productions, and studied Opera. She has a Bachelors degree in Acting and Directing and a Master's Degree in Information Technology She was published by America's foremost publisher of theatre arts books, and she has sold thousands of copies of the first edition of Sugared and Spiced 100 Monologues for Girls.

Jelliroll books that may interest you:

Sugared and Spiced 100 Monologues for Girls (1st edition)

Echo Booming Monologues 100 Monologues for Teens

Sugared and Spiced the Play: An Episodic Play in One Act for Girls

Echo Booming The Play An Episodic Play in One Act for Teens

Made in the USA
Middletown, DE
16 February 2021